IMPROVING REPAIRS AND MAINTENANCE SERVICES: A GOOD PRACTICE GUIDE

ANDREW THOMAS

PUBLISHED BY THE
CHARTERED INSTITUTE OF HOUSING
AND THE HOUSING CORPORATION

The Chartered Institute of Housing

The Chartered Institute of Housing (CIH) is the professional body for people involved in housing and communities. We are a registered charity and not-for-profit organisation. We have a diverse and growing membership of over 20,000 people – both in the public and private sectors - living and working in over 20 countries on five continents across the world. We exist to maximise the contribution that housing professionals make to the wellbeing of communities. Our vision is to be the first point of contact for – and the credible voice of – anyone involved or interested in housing.

Chartered Institute of Housing
Octavia House, Westwood Way
Coventry CV4 8JP
Telephone: 024 7685 1700
www.cih.org

The Housing Corporation

The Housing Corporation is the government agency which registers, regulates and funds over 1,500 social landlords in England which between them provide 2 million homes. The Corporation has an important role as a promoter of good practice in the social housing sector.

The Housing Corporation
149 Tottenham Court Road
London W1T 7BN
Telephone: 020 7393 2000
www.housingcorp.gov.uk

Improving Repairs and Maintenance Services: a good practice guide
Written by: Andrew Thomas
Editors: Jane Allanson
          Debbie Larner

© Chartered Institute of Housing and the Housing Corporation 2008
ISBN 978 1 905018 50 5

Graphic design by Jeremy Spencer
Cover photograph by Vincent Giordano/istockphoto.com
Printed by Alden Press

Contents

Introduction

by Dave Sheridan, UK managing director of Kier Building Maintenance

Kier Building Maintenance, a division of construction giant Kier Group, is fast establishing a reputation as the repairs and maintenance partner best-placed to assist housing organisations to improve their performance.

We credit our open, honest and communicative approach as the reason for its success.

We are well placed to support the ambitions of housing organisations countrywide; we currently maintain over 200,000 homes with over half a million responsive repairs carried out per year. Moreover, as part of the £2.1 billion turnover, we have the financial gravitas to invest in large and expert teams.

This approach – quality of people, quality of service – has earned Kier a raft of awards and commendations, in categories ranging from employability and diversity to health and safety.

This is also shown in our 'right first time on time' philosophy, where we ensure our processes and people are equipped to deliver excellent services.

This open communication is very much a 'top down' philosophy at Kier and tenants have direct access to our senior management in order to voice their concerns. This also results in the sharing of good practice across sites – some of which stems directly from tenants themselves – because they share the same vision and objectives.

Yet Kier's most cherished prize must be the trust of the people for whom we work. Kier cultivates positive working relationships with tenants, taking steps to ensure that they are involved in every part of a project, and that they remain happy with its services and people.

It was important to Kier that we worked with CIH on this authoritative guide because repairs and maintenance of housing is the service that touches people the most.

Any housing organisation aspiring to excellence must ensure its repair and maintenance programmes are of the highest standard as this is often where the people that matter will judge their housing service.

This is something that CIH recognises and something that Kier is proud to say has helped its clients improve star ratings and gain the coveted 3 star status.

Within the service, Kier works with local partners to develop education, training and employment opportunities for people who live in the areas in which we work. This is tailored to each partnership to ensure each client gets what they need to support the long term sustainability of their area. Diversity in employment and training practices and a firm focus on customer needs are key to Kier's leading-edge service.

In producing this guide with CIH, Kier intends to share its knowledge and experience to benefit everyone involved in the housing sector and to help raise standards across the board.

Acknowledgements

The research, writing and publication of this guide were supported by Housing Corporation IGP funding. We would like to thank Kier Group for its generous sponsorship, support and input into the guide. We have also received support from colleagues at Welsh Assembly Government and from the former Communities Scotland (now the Scottish Housing Regulator).

The following people gave their time to read and comment on the text at various stages; their feedback was much appreciated:

Angus Council	John Morrow
Audit Commission	Alison Brown
	Ron Price
CIH	Sarah Davis
	Debbie Larner
	John Perry
	Marie Vernon
Communities Scotland	Tessa Brown
	John Jenkins
	Gordon Smith
	Eleanor Sneddon
Consult CIH	Richard Medley
Flintshire Council	Pete Wynne
HouseMark	John Wickenden
Housing Corporation	Alison Mathias
Housing Ombudsman Service	Rafael Runco
Joseph Rowntree Trust	Norman Davidson
	Sally Houghton
Kier Group	Georgina Campbell
Kirklees Neighbourhood Housing Ltd	Paul Buckley
Local Government Ombudsman Service	Janet Aitken
Moray Council	Mike McClafferty
Scottish Public Services Ombudsman	Carolyn Hirst
SPH	John Bird

Thanks are also due to the many organisations and individuals who offered their views and experience and who contributed case studies and good practice examples to support this guide.

Final thanks to colleagues in the CIH policy and practice team who provided help and support throughout the production of this guide.

About the author

Andrew Thomas is a consultant specialising in asset management. He has worked with local authorities and housing associations throughout the UK, providing advice on public and private sector stock condition surveys and asset management strategies for housing and corporate resource accounting, together with renewal and affordable housing strategies. He undertakes due diligence reviews and option appraisals and is increasingly involved in data validation exercises and the manipulation of data to provide support for the delivery of planned maintenance programmes.

Andrew's previous experience includes housing association management roles in information systems, housing services and maintenance. Prior to this he was a lecturer at the Centre for Urban and Regional Studies, University of Birmingham, during which time he helped to set-up the international journal *Housing Studies* and the Housing Studies Association.

Andrew's recent publications are for the National Housing Federation on *Delivering Decent Homes* (2004), and the CIH report *Right First Time* on improving responsive repair services (2005). His various academic publications include a book on private sector urban renewal and papers on European approaches to asset management in social housing.

Andrew Thomas
andrew@assint.co.uk
Telephone 01962 810557 or 07786 243982

CHAPTER 1

INTRODUCTION

1.1 About this guide

Repairs and maintenance is one of the most important services provided by housing organisations. It is a service they are required to provide, and one that their tenants value. Research evidence backs experience on the ground; how tenants rate their landlord is influenced by what they think of the repairs service.

Therefore, to be successful, housing organisations need to provide a good repairs and maintenance service. Achieving this means doing the repairs which are requested, doing them promptly, and completing the job satisfactorily on the first visit. These are the basics, but being good means understanding what customers want and responding to their individual needs. Getting this right is important. It means being customer focused, involving tenants and offering choice.

Repairs and maintenance have to be done well but also efficiently. The service consumes a significant proportion of expenditure budgets. In combination, responsive and void repairs, cyclical maintenance and planned programmes represent a major element of the weekly rent. Even small gains in efficiency can translate into substantial savings.

In essence, the challenge for housing organisations is to provide a better service, that responds to the needs of their customers, and provides value for money. Housing organisations have found ways of providing a better service, and there are examples throughout the guide to reinforce the point. There are more repairs being done by appointment. There is a better chance that the repair will be done on the first visit. Some services are doing the work more quickly. There has been an intelligent use of technology to make it easier to report repairs through call centres; to make appointments using scheduling software; to allocate work more effectively through mobile working and to use text messaging to remind tenants of their appointments. Housing organisations are starting to use the web to make it easier for tenants to see the progress of their repair, to see planned programmes, and to compare their performance against others.

1.2 What does the guide aim to do?

The aim of this guide is to help local authorities, ALMOs and housing associations to look at ways to review and continuously improve the repairs and maintenance service that they deliver to their residents. The guide highlights good practice generally, providing case study evidence and signposts to other sources of information and guidance.

There is no single approach to providing a better repairs and maintenance service. This guide recognises that the way in which services are designed and delivered will vary according to the needs and wishes of tenants and the context within which these services are managed.

Because of this diversity, the guide is not a step-by-step legal or procedural manual to repairs and maintenance. The emphasis is on critical areas that define the nature of service provision and on which housing organisations should concentrate their attention. Generally, the guide is focused on the repairs and maintenance services provided to the *tenants* of social housing landlords, but there is reference to leaseholders where this is relevant to the specific chapter: for example, extending the repairs and maintenance service to leaseholders (Chapter 2); planned and programmed maintenance (Chapter 5); and asset management (Chapter 6).

The guide aims to support housing organisations to:
- Position their services in relation to the wider policy context
- Deliver a customer focused repairs and maintenance service
- Understand what factors influence a quality responsive and void repairs service
- Understand the drivers of demand for services
- Optimise the use of planned maintenance programmes
- Integrate asset management strategies with investment and business plans
- Consider the various options for procuring and delivering repairs and maintenance services
- Measure service quality
- Review and develop services to improve performance and meet new challenges.

The themes running through the guide are:

Understanding customer needs
Matching service to need is a concern that affects maintenance just like other services provided by housing organisations. Solutions differ; there is no one-size fits all in a diverse sector. It is important to know customers and to realise that their needs are not uniform.

The importance of communicating and working with customers

Involving tenants, but in ways that tenants want, provides direct benefits and increases choice. Planning and delivery of both responsive and planned maintenance cannot happen in a vacuum. It should be influenced by customer demand and their expectations of the service.

The value of working with the rest of the organisation

The repairs and maintenance function is not just a technical service working in isolation, it is a key part of the organisation's wider strategic and operational objectives. Recognising and resolving the sometimes conflicting demands of efficiency, regulatory requirements and customer demand requires organisational objectives to be clear and prioritised.

1.3 Who is the guide for?

The guide is aimed at a broad audience including policy makers who want to understand and respond to the changing context and environment in which services are delivered; performance managers responsible for continuous measurement and review; managers and staff responsible for implementing new and improved services; and front line staff who are responsible for delivering core services on the ground and who liaise directly with customers. It will also be a useful guide for board members when considering key issues, for example around organisational performance, procurement, investment planning and service review.

The focus on context and future delivery will be of interest to students of housing in general and also for students on courses that have a specific focus on housing maintenance. For example, the new housing maintenance qualifications developed by the CIOB-CIH Awarding Body.

The strong focus throughout the guide on customers will also make this a useful guide for the end users of repairs and maintenance services and those who are involved with their organisations to influence, shape and deliver services.

There are different policies in operation in England, Scotland and Wales, and there is no space to go into the detail. The social housing sector contains a diverse range of housing organisations, by size, region, function and philosophy. The focus of the guide is on good practice across the sector, drawing on common themes rather than looking at differences. The aim is to make general observations about the principles of service delivery, leaving each to work out how this applies to their own organisation. The guide is principally aimed at audiences in England, Scotland and Wales, however it is hoped that the content will be of use to other jurisdictions.

1.4 How is the guide organised?

The assumption is that most users of the guide will not read from front to back. They will dip in and out, taking from it what they need. There is, however, a sequence to the structure of the guide. The early chapters help to set a context and reinforce some of the key messages which run throughout the guide. The guide then moves on to consider some the 'core' elements of a repairs and maintenance service – responsive, void and planned. Following on from this, the guide focuses on strategic development, planning and delivery, considering asset management, procurement and partnering. The final chapters consider the key areas of performance and review, and look at the principles to be borne in mind when seeking to achieve service improvement.

Summarised chapter content:

- **Chapter 2** sets out a broad overview of the current environment in which housing organisations provide repairs and maintenance services, considering some of the key factors which influence the direction of change.

- **Chapter 3** looks at how organisations can develop a customer focused repairs service, considering issues such as choice, feedback and customer insight.

- **Chapter 4** focuses on the key requirements of a good quality responsive repairs service considering the importance of core areas such as repairs reporting, appointment systems, use of information technology and mobile working. This section also covers void repairs.

- **Chapter 5** looks specifically at planned maintenance including strategic planning, implementation and delivery. This section also covers gas servicing.

- **Chapter 6** considers asset management in its strategic context, particularly in relation to investment planning, portfolio performance and also wider neighbourhood planning.

- **Chapter 7** looks at how services are procured and the way in which services are delivered and managed. It specifically covers the areas of procurement and partnering in relation to repairs and maintenance.

- **Chapter 8** considers how to measure performance and service quality, both from the perspective of the organisation in terms of assessing value for money and from that of the customer in terms of providing appropriate and effective services.

- **Chapter 9** focuses on service review and development. It looks at the key stages and processes of a review and sets out some suggested methodologies illustrated by case studies.

- **Chapter 10** brings together the principles to be considered by housing organisations who are aiming to improve their repairs and maintenance service.

1.5 Definitions and terms used in the guide

Throughout the guide, the generic terms *social housing* and *housing organisation* are used to refer to the affordable housing sector and the providers of affordable rented housing respectively. Their principal customers are referred to as *tenants*, not to define their legal status, but to distinguish them from shared owners, leaseholders, or in Scotland, owners of flats in mixed-ownership blocks. The term *resident* is used when referring to the wider community (including tenants, leaseholders and home owners) and the term *customer* is used specifically when considering the experiences of the repairs and maintenance service.

The term *contractor* is used as short-hand for both external contractors (under partnering or traditional contracts) and internal DSOs (including joint ventures).

The following broad definitions are included for the purpose of this guide; readers are reminded that 'repair' and 'improvement' have precise definitions established in law. A summary of the core legislation can be found at the end of this chapter. For further detailed information refer to the repairs and maintenance chapter of the CIH online housing manual **www.cih.org/housingmanual**.

Responsive and void repairs: maintenance arising from the landlord's obligation to carry out repairs to a property arising from:

- A tenant's request (emergency, urgent or routine repairs)
- Unanticipated major works, for example, related to fire, flood or other weather damage
- Repairs to empty properties before letting.

Planned maintenance: the renewal of components that are at the end of their useful life. It can also refer to any works that are not responsive, including improvements to external or internal elements, or to the curtilage and wider external environment. The key characteristics, therefore, are that works are predicted and delivered as part of a programme. Related to this is cyclical maintenance and service contracts. 'Cyclical' has no fixed definition, but is used for programmes on a periodic cycle such as re-painting, annual gas safety checks or quarterly fire equipment inspections.

Asset management: the management of physical assets to meet an organisation's service and financial objectives. Good asset management will ensure that the housing stock meets current and future needs, including planning for investment in repairs and improvements and reviewing and changing the portfolio in response to local circumstances.

The core legislation

Repairs and maintenance

The main legislation governing landlords' responsibilities for the repair and maintenance of rented property is:

- The Landlord and Tenant Act 1985 (Section 8 and Section 11), which also covers consultation with leaseholders
- The Defective Premises Act 1972 – duties of reasonable care in relation to works
- Environmental Protection Act 1990 – control of premises considered prejudicial to health or a nuisance. Local authority and housing association tenants have statutory nuisance provisions to obtain improvements and repairs
- Housing (Scotland) Act 2001 – Section 27 and Schedule 4 requires landlords of secure tenancies to ensure the house is wind and water tight and reasonably fit for habitation throughout the tenancy
- Right to Repair Regulations 1994 – gives English and Welsh local authority secure tenants the right to compensation if certain repairs are not undertaken within a prescribed period. This was granted to housing association tenants under Housing Corporation circular 33/94. The equivalent in Scotland is the Secure Tenants (Right to Repairs) Regulations 2002
- The Commonhold and Leasehold Reform Act 2002 – the right to manage and consultation about service charges.

Health and safety legislation

- Building Regulations 2000 (as amended) applies to England and Wales
- Building (Scotland) Act 2003 is the equivalent legislation in Scotland
- Construction (Design and Management) Regulations 2007
- The Gas Safety (Installation and Use) Regulations 1998 requires all landlords to undertake an annual safety check of gas appliances
- Control of Asbestos Regulations 2006
- Housing Act 2004 introduced the Housing Health and Safety Rating System
- Corporate Manslaughter and Corporate Homicide Act 2007.

Discrimination and disability legislation

- Disability Discrimination Act 1995, requiring that the delivery of repairs and maintenance services do not discriminate against disabled people in the household. The Disability Discrimination Act 2005 introduced further requirements, including making reasonable adjustments to properties
- Housing Grants, Construction and Regeneration Act 1996 places a duty on local authorities to provide Disabled Facilities Grants
- Housing (Scotland) Act 2006 gives private sector tenants the right to adapt their home so that it is suitable accommodation.

→

Directives on energy efficiency
- Home Energy Conservation Act 1995 – requires local authorities to identify and report on energy conservation measures
- EU directives on energy performance in buildings (EPBD, see **www.diag.org.uk**)
- Energy Performance Certificates required prior to re-letting. In England and Wales this is linked to HIPs, with the enabling powers being SI 2007 No 1669. In Scotland the Scottish Building Standards Agency operates under the Building (Scotland) Act 2003 and the Building (Scotland) Amendment Regulations 2006.

Directives on EU procurement
- Public contract regulations 2006 set out the rules of tendering works and supplies of services above values reviewed annually (see for example HAIAF, 2006a).

CHAPTER 2

THE POLICY CONTEXT

This chapter sets out a broad overview of the current environment in which housing organisations provide the repairs and maintenance services to residents and considers how changes will impact on the way these services are shaped and delivered both now and in the future.

2.1 Core functions

A good quality repairs and maintenance service and a strong asset management strategy are core functions of housing providers. This will remain true under any change to policy or regulatory functions over the foreseeable future. Indeed, the current policy agenda emphasises the importance of service quality, meeting customer needs and responding to future requirements.

All housing organisations have direct statutory responsibilities to their tenants for repairs and maintenance, and have a general duty to ensure that their repairs and maintenance services do not result in discrimination against people with disabilities. Repairs services are also required to conform to the wider obligations of housing organisations as contained within equalities, race relations and procurement legislation.

The impact that a piece of legislation may have will vary depending on the type and scale of repair and maintenance works being undertaken, and on the actual duties placed on housing organisations within any specific piece of legislation.

A summary of the core legislation can be found at the end of Chapter 1. For more detail refer to the repairs and maintenance chapter of the CIH online housing manual **www.cih.org/housingmanual.**

As well as providing a repair service that meets statutory requirements, housing organisations have legal duties in relation to the adequacy and suitability of their homes. The property must be in a good state of repair, and achieve minimum health and safety standards linked to public health legislation. Housing organisations must conform to heating and electrical safety testing regulations. Void properties must be let in a safe and reasonable condition. And all property must conform to a minimum quality standard set by government.

The term 'housing quality standard' is used throughout this guide as a generic description to include the different arrangements in England, Scotland and Wales. The English Decent Homes Standard (DHS) was introduced in the 2000 Housing Green Paper (DETR), carrying the commitment that all social housing must exceed specified standards by 2010 (the most recent guidance is CLG, 2006). The Welsh Housing Quality Standard followed (Welsh Assembly Government, 2002a) with a target of 2012. Finally, Scotland defined a standard to be delivered by 2015 (Communities Scotland, 2004).

As the first, the English Decent Homes Standard helped to set objectives and encourage a more strategic approach to asset management (NHF, 2004a; CLG, 2007). There have been problems with data quality (CLG, 2007), raising questions about the ability of housing organisations to target the delivery of the standard, and to demonstrate compliance. There have also been criticisms of the standard itself: that it is low in terms of thermal comfort; pays insufficient attention to the immediate environment outside the home; and fails to address questions of sustainability.

The standards in Scotland and Wales are different, with the WHQS including factors concerned with a safe and attractive environment. There are discussions in England about a possibly revised and enhanced post-2010 Decent Homes Standard. A more comprehensive standard would set the bar higher, and with it the costs of conforming. But even without change to the minimum standard most housing organisations will have a 'decent homes plus' standard developed in consultation with tenants and responding to their own local circumstances (Housing Corporation, 2007c). This will consider environmental and sustainability issues and might address accessibility by taking account, where possible, of the Lifetime Homes Standard.

For more on lifetime homes see:
- **www.lifetimehomes.org.uk**
- **www.jrf.org.uk/housingandcare/lifetimehomes**

Strong asset management strategies are crucial to the long term maintenance of the stock and the financial viability of the organisation. This is about the management of physical assets, ensuring that investment is made to meet long term needs (see Chapter 6), but it is also about delivering standards that meet the aspirations of existing and future tenants.

2.2 The role of regulation

The regulation of social housing is changing, with more focus on housing organisations meeting the needs of tenants, and giving tenants more power to register dissatisfaction with the quality of service they receive.

The new regulatory regime

In England, following the Cave Review of regulation (CLG, 2007a), the Housing and Regeneration Bill (November 2007) provided for the creation of a new housing regulator, OFTENANT, and a new housing and regeneration agency, the Homes and Communities Agency (HCA). HCA combines the investment role of the Housing Corporation, all of English Partnerships and the delivery work of CLG on Decent Homes, PFI and Housing Market Renewal.

OFTENANT takes over the regulatory functions of the Housing Corporation for housing associations, with the government's stated intention to introduce a domain approach to regulation by bring local authority housing (including ALMOs) into the same regime. OFTENANT will have new powers, and a greater focus on ensuring tenants receive a good service and will use inspection as one of its regulatory tools.

In Scotland the intention is to create a new social housing regulatory function that is focused on protecting and promoting the interests of current and future tenants, that reduces the burden of regulation and inspection on local authorities and housing associations, and that exercises its powers independently of Ministers (Scottish Government, 2007). From April 2008, the performance standards to be achieved by local authorities and housing associations are measured and monitored by the Scottish Housing Regulator.

Local government performance framework

In England, from April 2008, Best Value performance measures have been replaced with a new performance framework which moves away from national targets to local accountability within a national framework of scrutiny. The new indicators and associated targets (CLG, 2007c) will be adopted by local authorities, but other organisations will contribute to their delivery through Local Strategic Partnerships (LSPs), Local Area Agreements (LAAs) and the Sustainable Community Strategy (SCS).

Local Area Agreements (LAA)

Housing organisations will contribute to the delivery of the new national indicators through LAAs. The Local Government and Public Involvement in Health Act 2007 provides the statutory basis for LAAs. It introduces a new duty on local authorities to involve local people in local services, and a duty on named partners to co-operate in the agreement of targets and to take account of these targets in their work. Because of the focus on outcomes it seems likely that local authorities will be looking at whether housing organisations are providing a quality services that respond to local need.

Comprehensive Area Assessments (CAA)

To support the new performance framework, Comprehensive Area Assessments (CAA) will be introduced in 2009, replacing Comprehensive Performance Assessments (CPA). The new CAA are intended to look at the services delivered in an area by local authorities and their partners, including the private and voluntary sectors. CAAs will focus the emphasis on how well a local area is meeting particular needs and community priorities and will highlight where providers are not delivering public services that are responsive to the needs of local communities. The aim is to be more relevant to local people by focusing on what is important to the local community. Again, the requirement on housing organisations is to be aware of the needs, views and aspirations of its tenants and the communities within which they work.

The Hills Review on the future roles of social housing (2007) highlighted the need for more integration of housing and employment support. The Government's response to some of the challenges raised by the review include:

- *Housing and employment advice:* Five pilots to look at tackling financial exclusion and worklessness amongst social housing tenants
- *HRA review:* A review of the Housing Revenue Account subsidy system
- *Review of PRS:* A review of the private rented sector to identify more and better private sector options.

2.3 The direction of change

The changed focus of regulation is an indicator of broader developments. While good quality repairs and maintenance services and robust asset management strategies will remain a core function of all housing organisations, the environment in which they are delivered is going through a period of significant change. More attention is being paid to customer focus, tenant involvement and choice. At the same time, there are pressures on costs with further demands to demonstrate efficiencies and policies to increase the supply of affordable housing.

These changes will impact on what and how services are shaped and delivered both now and in the future. The following sections set out some of the broader changes. Chapter 9 will consider in more detail how organisations can respond by developing and adapting their services.

Efficiency targets

Following the Gershon Review in 2004, CLG set targets for efficiency gains across the public sector. These targets related to what were referred to as both cashable and non-cashable gains. The aim was to increase resources going to front-line services. The 2007 Comprehensive Spending Review set tougher targets. Local authorities and housing associations in England are expected to achieve 3% net cash-releasing value for money gains every year for the next three years.

The need for efficiency is encouraging housing organisations to explore ways of simplifying processes, achieving economies of scale and developing different kinds of partnership.

More homes

Following the Barker Review (HM Treasury, 2004) the Green Paper for England (CLG, 2007b) responded to evidence of demand by proposing to provide more homes and more affordable homes to rent and buy. Though patterns of demand are different in Scotland and Wales there are similar concerns about the supply of affordable housing (see for example Scottish Government, 2007).

This policy direction has potential implications for the funding available to maintain the existing stock. One concern is the pressure on business plans to show they can support higher levels of debt by under-estimating future maintenance liabilities. In England, Housing Corporation capacity estimates acknowledge competing priorities, and that investment in the existing stock is something Boards need to consider against the funding of new development (Housing Corporation, 2007:5). The greater involvement of tenants and community empowerment are also factors that can influence the balance of decisions about new development and re-investment.

Customer focus

Government emphasises that organisations delivering public services must be responsive to the needs and aspirations of communities and this is reflected in the changed regulatory regime described above. In England, the Local Government White Paper (CLG, 2006b) aimed to give local people and local communities more influence and power to improve their lives. It signalled a devolution from the centre because of the inadequacy of older 'one size fits all' service models. The White Paper stated that people wanted choice over the service they received, influence over those who provide them, and higher service standards.

A similar emphasis is found in the Audit Commission's Key Lines of Enquiry (KLOEs). The presentation of these changed in August 2007 to encourage housing organisations to find their own route to providing excellent service. Under *Stock Investment and Asset Management* there is an emphasis on access, customer care and user focus. Comments on excellent service highlight the need to consult, to identify and to recognise the needs of different users, and to apply this knowledge of customer needs as a way of driving the improvement of service delivery.

In Wales *Making the Connections* (WAG, 2006c) is an action plan for improving public service delivery. This aims to involve people in the design, delivery and improvement of public services, and follows the Beecham Review (WAG, 2006d) which linked improved engagement and better service delivery. *Making the Connections* seeks to include people in shaping and scrutinising services, measuring satisfaction, strengthening partnerships and finding ways to give people a stronger voice in shaping services and priorities to meet current and future needs.

In Scotland, the discussion document *Firm Foundations* (Scottish Government, 2007) suggests that the role of tenants should be strengthened so that they can become more empowered customers. Building on the Crerar Review (2007) it advocates a regulatory regime that promotes and protects the interests of current and future tenants, engages with these service customers and involves them in the scrutiny process.

Customer focus is considered in more detail in Chapter 3.

Community empowerment and choice

The Hills Review (2007) recognised that the needs of tenants were different and varied over time. Basing service delivery on individual circumstances and requirements starts by knowing what the customer wants. This is crucial to much of the new policy context. Government takes the view that giving tenants a greater say leads to more effective, efficient and responsive services.

Tenant involvement takes many forms. It ranges from developing service standards, through scrutiny of performance, to active involvement in management.

Community involvement and empowerment means giving local people choices about what happens in the area where they live. A finding of the Elton Commission, the Tenants Involvement Commission (NHF, 2006), and Martin Cave's Every Tenant Matters review (CLG, 2007a) was that tenants expressed a huge appetite for choice. In terms of the maintenance service tenants were looking for more choice about appointment times, picking contractors and dismissing contractors if they did not perform. They did not want to pay more for a basic service, though they did indicate interest in being able to pay for extras.

Tenants cannot leave their landlord without leaving their home, and doing this within the social housing sector can be difficult and realistically impossible in areas of high demand. A recommendation of the Cave Review was that the new regulator should have a duty to expand the availability of choice of provider. The motive was to allow tenants to exercise more choice in a variety of ways, including choice over different types of service and choice over the management organisation.

> *'As with other industries, there is scope for improving effectiveness by 'unbundling' – ie having the various activities performed by different organisations…Diversity of provision could be particularly vibrant and beneficial for tenants in relation to the management of social housing. Owners could contract management to other providers, or to specialist public or private sector management firms.'* (CLG, 2007a:21).

The radical approach is to allow the tenant to stay in their home but choose a different landlord or service provider. This separation of ownership and management is only an option, but one commentator has suggested:

> *'There is a strong case for local communities to own their own homes. This does not mean that management and renewal need to run to the same scale. Ownership, staffing and control ought to be unbundled: community-owned estates could be perfectly well served by staff whose role is to buy in services. Uncoupling social ownership and staffing offers the real possibility of restructuring housing management. Why should services be provided separately to council and association tenants and stop at municipal boundaries? It would be truly revolutionary for management to be rethought as a competitive industry, integrated with the private rental and private ownership sectors.'* (Maclennan, 2007)

There are parallels here with community and mutual housing associations, but these operate in the context of joint ownership, rather than offering choice of service provider without a change of ownership. An alternative is a lease-back from existing housing organisations to locally based organisations who contract-out housing management services. This could be a method of consolidating local service provision without transferring stock ownership. Such an approach is consistent with recent research on stock restructuring (CIH, 2007a:13). What needs to be considered very carefully is whether it would produce better service at lower costs.

Environmental performance

New build has seen a series of measures and targets to improve environmental performance, most notably the aim to achieve zero carbon residential developments by 2016 through a gradual tightening of Building Regulations linked to the Code for Sustainable Homes (CLG, 2006c). A mandatory rating against the Code is required for all new homes. What needs to be anticipated is whether there are any longer term maintenance costs associated with the new homes designed to meet improved levels of sustainability (see for example Code Level 6 described in CLG, 2006c).

Whilst the bar has been raised in terms of the environmental performance of new build, there is not currently the same focus on existing stock. Annual new build accounts for only about one per cent of the national housing stock, while the vast majority of homes built before 2000 will still be in use in fifty years time. The challenge is to improve the existing stock in an informed and affordable way. One pointer would be for organisations to take note of new build requirements and the Code for Sustainable Homes when framing their decent homes plus standard.

The Energy Performance of Buildings Directive has become one of the main instruments to encourage the improved energy efficiency of existing buildings. The Directive requires an Energy Performance Certificate (EPC) for a building every time it is sold or rented. From October 2008, EPCs will come into force in the social and private rented sector in England. Since the Directive lacks any 'regulatory teeth' (there is no obligation to implement the recommendations in an EPC), there are questions about its effectiveness in improving the energy efficiency of the existing stock on the scale needed.

EPCs will however provide organisations with a good indication of the environmental performance of the stock, which might be linked to the adoption of EcoHomes XB. The challenge is to move from measurement to improvement. Whilst many organisations will have implemented the more cost-effective measures (cavity wall and loft insulation, double glazing, efficient boilers) anything over and above, such as micro-generation technology, will incur much higher initial costs with as yet unknown payback profiles.

Mixed tenure

One of the consequence of RTB is that ownership of conventional estates has become more fragmented and the delivery of a 'decent places' agenda therefore more complex. The implication of growth in mixed tenure is that maintenance services will operate in a more varied pattern of ownership. There will be an increased number of owners and part-owners of flats who are customers of planned and cyclical maintenance services and who can report responsive repairs for common areas. At the same time there are trends which are tending to increase the costs of service charges, including the more widespread use of CCTV and more sophisticated door entry and fire protection systems. As a result, service charge management will become a more visible area of activity.

Leaseholders (owners in Scotland) must be consulted individually or as a group. Thought is required about the desirability and practicality of making future provision against exceptional works, and with this, whether in some circumstances a form of resident management company might be a sensible approach. Under the Local Government White Paper (CLG, 2006b) Tenant Management Organisations (TMOs) are to be encouraged, with a proposed simplification of the Right to Manage, but this does not seem to address the management of mixed tenure schemes. Similarly the Cave review (CLG, 2007a) is concerned with protecting and empowering tenants, but says little about the way enhancing tenant choice engages with a mixed-tenure agenda.

The growth of mixed tenure again asks the question whether there are opportunities to widen the repairs and maintenance services to home owners. If a housing organisation is offering a repairs service to tenants in a block of flats it might seem a management advantage and business opportunity to offer the service to all residents. One example is a leaseholders and home owners repair service in Lambeth. This is an extension of the repair service already provided to tenants, with owners paying for time and material.

The idea of cross-tenure service is not new. What might have changed is that housing organisations are now better at delivering a specialist service, have the systems in place to extend their reach, and are starting to work in a mixed tenure environment where such a service offers mutual benefits. The charging system needs careful thought, as does the management framework within which it operates in leasehold estates.

2.4 Skills for the new role

If housing organisations are to work in new ways, this makes demands on skills in terms of managing service delivery. For example, the management of external resources in the context of partnering presents a different balance of contract management, technical skills and customer focus. The requirement is for skills in negotiation, commissioning, contract monitoring and financial management. External contractors may be providing the main elements of customer-facing services for responsive and planned works. Their training and development needs are not under the direct control of the client, but standards of customer care have to be agreed and monitored.

The demand for skills applies to moving into new areas of work:

- The role of housing organisations in the wider task of community regeneration and community development (HM Treasury, 2006)
- The role of housing organisations in a world of changed tenure, and the skills required to deliver service, for example, repairs services to leaseholders.

Staff development is fundamental to service quality because it is people that deliver the service. Within housing organisations the priorities are to work on culture and values, the use of skills audits and staff training and development. If existing staff do not have the skills, they have to be trained or new skills recruited.

For the sector as a whole, recruitment and retention of people with the right skills presents short term difficulties. The Egan Skills Review looked for change in the skills base to deliver sustainable communities, leadership, teamwork, communication and partnership working. The skills required would seem to be in very short supply. There have been a number of sector wide initiatives aimed at developing skills (Green, 2004:11-13), but to these need to be added specific initiatives in the field of maintenance and asset management.

> In order to bring in and retain new and technically qualified people into the field, CIH and the CIOB have launched a joint programme of new technical qualifications in housing maintenance. These range from a Level 2 (GCSE equivalent) certificate in Housing Maintenance to a Level 4 (HNC equivalent) Diploma in Housing Maintenance and Asset Management or in Housing Development.
>
> See **www.cih.org/education** for more information.

2.5 Keeping ahead of the game

The future direction and rate of change is perhaps of only passing concern to those faced with the immediate pressure of improving service performance. But if the trends are understood and properly embraced there is a good chance that proposed service enhancements will be on the right side of the curve. Those who can see the direction of change are in a better position to control events. Organisations need to be anticipating and innovating in areas that may soon be requirements for change.

Summary

- The repairs and maintenance service is expected to meet standards set by regulators, to perform against criteria defined by an inspection framework, to respond to the requirements and expectations of tenants, to be part of a process of continuous improvement and contribute to an agenda of efficiency savings.

- The changing regulatory regime gives greater emphasis to meeting the needs of tenants, and gives tenants more power to register dissatisfaction with the service they receive.

- The new local government performance framework aims for more local accountability, with new duties to involve local people in local services.

- The review of regulation raises the need for more choice. This might, in the future, open up the option of separating ownership from service provision.

- The policy of increasing housing supply, together with the need for efficiency savings, is placing additional pressures on budgets to maintain the existing stock.

- The drive for more affordable housing is also likely to increase the proportion of mixed tenure schemes. Service delivery and service charge management in mixed tenure schemes is a growing area of activity and complexity.

- While development and maintenance compete for limited resources there are other cost pressures in the form of higher standards of thermal efficiency and sustainability.

- Change has been a recurrent theme for housing organisations over the past few years. This does not seem likely to abate. It demands that organisations keep abreast of events, and have the skills to respond to changes in the pattern of service delivery.

CHAPTER 3

CUSTOMER FOCUS

In order to deliver a customer focused service, it is important that organisations know who their customers are, what these customers consider are the essential requirements of a good service, and how they want the service to develop and evolve. It is also valuable to have an understanding of who currently uses the repairs service, and how frequently, as this will support decisions about service design and delivery costs. A range of methods can be used to gain information, from customer involvement and feedback, through surveys, customer audits and mystery shopping.

3.1 Defining a good service – the customer perspective

The repairs and maintenance service is very important to tenants. There is a clear link between satisfaction with the repairs service and overall satisfaction with the housing organisation. For example a Housing Corporation survey showed that amongst those tenants who were satisfied with the repairs service, 91% were satisfied with the overall service provided by their housing organisation. Looking only at those who were dissatisfied with the repairs service, just 28% were satisfied with the overall service (Housing Corporation, 2006a:11).

The NHF's Tenant Involvement Commission found tenants wanted repairs to take place in an acceptable timeframe; to know exactly when to expect the repair to be done; to be contacted and given an explanation if the repair was not to be done in the agreed time; and for the repair to be carried out to a high standard without the need for further and repeat work (NHF, 2006:13). The Commission commented that it was a myth that service users asked for the earth. In fact the real risk was that many would not ask for much at all. Overall, tenants' demand of a good housing organisation was just to get services right, and to do this right first time, every time.

Right First Time

A CIH study (*Right First Time*, CIH, 2005) looked at how housing associations were improving the quality of their responsive repairs services. The research examined tenants' views about a good repairs service. It found that tenants value a service that offers an appointment; keeps the appointment; and completes work to a good standard. If an appointment has to be changed they want to be told. And they do not want to have to report the fault more than once. Further details on delivering a good quality responsive repairs service can be found in Chapter 4.

The CIH report found that tenants did not particularly want to be involved in the management of the service, but they did want their experience of the service to be taken into account. What tenants wanted was that their housing organisation should:

- Get the basics right – understand customers in all their diversity and know their preferences and circumstances

- Give choice – listen to people and act on this

- Make involvement personal

- Be accountable – give tenants an opportunity to have a voice in decisions, whether at neighbourhood or strategic level.

There is a consistent set of messages here, reinforced by a Cabinet Office MORI survey that identified five factors shaping satisfaction across a wide range of public services (OPSR, 2004). In order of importance these are:

- Delivery – of the promised outcome and the handling of any problems that arise

- Timeliness – responding immediately to initial contact, dealing with the issue at the heart of it quickly and without passing it on

- Information – providing accurate and comprehensive information, keeping customers informed about progress

- Professionalism – competent staff treating customers fairly

- Staff attitude – polite and friendly staff, sympathetic to customer needs.

The CIH report *Right First Time* is available from **www.cih.org/policy/ RightFirstTime05.pdf**

Defining a good repairs service – HouseMark

In researching their guidance on local performance measures (HouseMark, 2008a) tenant focus groups were asked to define what they considered to be a 'good' repairs service. The following were considered to form the foundations:

Information and communication
- Clearly set out responsibilities of both the tenant and the landlord
- Clear priority structure (for example, emergencies differentiated from other repairs)
- Clear procedures for reporting repairs, including details about appointments
- Notification of delayed or cancelled appointments
- Good quality information and feedback on service standards and performance against those standards
- Knowledge (by everyone) of repair timescales and repairs procedure.

Customer care
- Certainty that contractors will turn up and do what was agreed at the agreed time
- Convenience and choice over time slot
- The job done in one visit where possible and with no mess
- Quality of contact in reporting a responsive repair:
  - politeness and competence of staff
  - ease of access
  - confidence in the system
- Quality of contact in terms of the operative
- Code of conduct for contractors which is adhered to
- Good appointment system with choice, flexibility and with penalties for contractor and tenant if either fail to keep the appointment
- Choice of improvements, fixtures, fittings, finishing/decorations
- Good out-of-hours service
- Follow-up satisfaction surveys
- Inspections carried out to check standards
- Levels of tenant satisfaction monitored and fed back on.

Value for money
- An intelligent approach to maintaining the stock focused on planned replacement
- The job done right first time, without the need for follow-on work – ideally operatives should have discretion to adapt job descriptions if necessary to get the job done and even take the opportunity to proactively address any other quick jobs within time slot.

→

Consultation and involvement
- Involvement in setting standards and prioritisation of repairs
- Involvement in setting terms for contracts and in selecting contractors.

Meeting specific needs
- Up-to-date knowledge of who the customer is so that specific needs and preferences can be reflected in service delivery (for example, a disabled customer may take some time to answer the door; a female customer may prefer not to be alone with a male operative).

Adapted from *How to develop and monitor local performance measures: a guide for tenants and landlords*, HouseMark, 2008

Delivering excellence

The Audit Commission sets out the following descriptors in relation to access, customer care and user focus. An excellent housing organisation should:
- Have staff that all demonstrate user focus in their work, who treat people with respect at all times.
- Have front-line staff that demonstrate a wide range of knowledge about the full range of enquiries they receive or know who or how to access the necessary information to help service users.
- Make it easy for residents to report or query repairs or improvements by telephone, in person or electronically, including outside normal office hours – all of which are dealt with efficiently and effectively.
- Use appropriate technology to help staff and service users identify the appropriate repair.
- Tell service users when their repair should be completed at the time they report it, including outside normal office hours.
- Arrange repair, maintenance and improvement work, and inspections related to it, at a time to suit the service user, mainly by appointment.
- Tell service users and leaseholders whether they are responsible for paying the cost of a repair at the time they report it.
- Have clear arrangements for dealing with service users when they refuse access for repairs and uses appropriate legal methods to ensure the completion of all necessary works.
- Have published clear service standards for the repairs service, which are tailored to meet local need and which often exceed minimum statutory requirements; for example, Right to Repair for council service users.

→

- Actively canvas the views of service users and uses them to review or improve services. Service users are consulted and involved in major decisions that affect the service, for example in relation to stock investment priorities, programmes and procurement and repairs target timescales.
- Have service users who feel confident that their input will be valued and acted upon.
- Have service users who are satisfied with the repairs and improvements they receive and this is evidenced by a wide range of feedback methods.

Audit Commission KLOE: *Landlord services: Stock Investment and Asset Management* (2004)

3.2 Involving residents

Housing organisations should involve and consult residents on all aspects of the repairs and maintenance service. Residents are better able to identify options and make choices when provided with the relevant information needed to inform their views. It is reasonable that housing organisations show very clearly the budgets they have for repairs and maintenance and how this is funded. Tenants will see what proportion of their rent goes on repairs and maintenance and should be able to influence the priorities, assess value for money and monitor service quality.

Effective consultation and involvement means using a variety of approaches, from tenant representatives, through consultative panels to neighbourhood or estate associations. The framework might include:

- Consultations on:
    - service standards, including prioritisation and target timescales
    - choice of components
    - procurement options
    - investment priorities
    - neighbourhood management reviews
- Resident involvement activities around estate management
- Service contract monitoring or customer audits
- Satisfaction with repairs reporting processes and the effectiveness of appointment systems
- Comments, complaints and compliments schemes
- Post inspection and post repairs completion surveys
- Staff suggestions.

These mechanisms do not involve structures specific to repairs and maintenance, and the fullest possible use should be made of existing frameworks in order to canvas the views of a wide cross section of service users.

Systems and frameworks are a necessary part of involvement and consultation. But the best involvement is not an add-on; it forms part of the process. This comes down to how the individual tenant feels they have been treated when using the service. It means that the staff and contractors they come in contact with have a focus on customers. It means a real commitment from front-line staff and this includes the contractors as well. Find out what they hear from tenants and encourage them to seek their own service improvements. The people at the front-end are the first to know what is going wrong, and it will not get fixed without their help.

3.3 Customer feedback

There are a variety of methods for gaining customer feedback and measuring customer satisfaction. It is not a question of deciding which one to use. A variety of techniques are needed.

Gentoo – Monitoring satisfaction

Gentoo Sunderland has introduced a plan of continuous customer monitoring for repairs satisfaction. The plan is a rolling six monthly programme incorporating a diverse range of methods of measuring customer satisfaction in an attempt to engage with as many customers as possible.

Some of the feedback mechanisms run throughout the six month programme (for example, telephone surveys, customer experience questionnaires, complaints, etc.). In addition each month attention is focused on a particular aspect of the service.

This includes using UDCs (User Defined Characteristics that record customer equality and diversity monitoring data) to provide a profile of customers using the repairs service, comparing that profile to regional information held and using that information to generate a representative sample of customers to survey.

Other ways to gain feedback include surveying previous complainants (to establish an increase in their satisfaction levels), using the website to gather feedback, targeting certain trades or priorities in need of further analysis depending upon the results of analysing customer feedback received.

→

In addition to the existing methods available, Gentoo is currently scoping the use of handhelds to gather customer satisfaction data and the introduction of a customer experience questionnaire specific to this service area.

As well as using all of the data collected to identify service improvements, the positive comments being received from customers are fed back to individuals who are praised for delivering an excellent level of service.

Service delivery checks

Service delivery checks are a good way to get feedback, particularly for responsive repairs, because the experience is fresh in tenants' minds. Historically this involved completion of a satisfaction card left by the tradesperson. This has several disadvantages as the responsibility is placed on the tenant to take action to return the card and often returns can be unrepresentative. Increasingly, telephone checks are used by housing organisations. Selective sampling can reduce the cost of this method.

Questions should cover different stages of the repairs reporting process, such as:
- Experience of reporting a repair
- Appointment reliability
- Quality and standard of completed repair.

Questions can be weighted, or adjusted to give a score and provide a measure that can be understood and tracked over time. Data should be analysed and reported to staff, partners and customers on a regular basis.

Satisfaction surveys

While satisfaction cards or telephone checks report the most recent service users' experience, satisfaction surveys can place the whole thing in context in order to understand how the repair and maintenance service is viewed in terms of a range of other factors. There are three limitations. First, a general attitude survey such as STATUS cannot devote much space to repairs and maintenance, so coverage lacks depth. Second, surveys are typically conducted infrequently. In principle they can inform service reviews but they are not intended for day-to-day monitoring of service performance. Third, survey questionnaires ask pre-determined questions which exclude views being gathered on areas not covered.

Qualitative surveys can help provide a more comprehensive and up to date picture. Properly conducted, they are a powerful tool for gaining insight into a range of service problems. They are particularly useful to inform service reviews on a periodic basis.

Guidance on customer research

In England, social landlords are expected to complete a satisfaction survey at least every three years. The standard methodology is STATUS (Standardised Tenant Satisfaction Survey), developed by the NHF (2000). The Housing Corporation explicitly expect housing associations to follow the STATUS methodology.

There is no standardised tenant satisfaction indicator currently in use in Scotland, but Communities Scotland (2006) published guidance for landlords on gathering service user views on service quality. This includes advice on satisfaction surveys, qualitative research and the use of complaints as feedback.

The National Consumer Council (NCC) published a *Playlist for public services* in 2005 as a guide to public service design. This advocates the measurement and reporting of customer satisfaction in a consistent and systematic way.

Also in 2005 the Local Government Association published *Putting the customer first* which highlighted the key success factors in the use of customer information.

In 2007 the NCC and Local Government Association published *Customer satisfaction with local services*, emphasising the importance of putting customers first and collecting high-quality, up-to-date information about customers as an essential tool for the delivery of local services.

Mystery shopping

Increasing numbers of organisations are developing mystery customer schemes, using their own tenants and residents as mystery shoppers. Arrangements are also emerging between groups of housing organisations who are working in partnership to assess and benchmark the services delivered by the other organisations. This provides tenants with an opportunity to view and compare standards of service between different housing organisations.

A guide to mystery shopping can be found in the Housing Corporation report *Mystery Shopping at the ACIS Group: Toolkit for improving standards*. The subject is also referenced in Communities Scotland (2006).

Tenant auditors

The use of tenants as auditors is becoming more widespread. Groups of tenants are trained to look at the services provided by their housing organisation and make recommendations about how the service can be improved.

Tenant auditors

The Wrekin Trust

The tenant audit is an integral element of tenant involvement at the Trust and a core method of improving services. The results are:

- Auditors have offered practical ideas and recommendations that have led to positive service improvements

- The project has attracted individuals not previously involved in tenant participation

- The Trust's performance indicators are customer verified

- Understanding and relationships between staff and tenants have been improved.

West Lothian Council

The Council involves tenants in service improvements through short life working groups involving tenants and staff, Quality Improvement Teams (QITs) and comprehensive Tenant Led Inspections (TLIs). The council convenes a QIT to focus on a particular service area. It looks at the structure of the service, its objectives, its performance indicators and outcomes. Overall its purpose is to identify areas for improvement.

TLIs set their own inspection programme and look in detail at what is really happening in service delivery and whether the service meets tenants' needs and expectations. The TLI report makes recommendations for improvements to the council and the council responds to these recommendations. TLI have previously examined the repairs service, neighbourhood response teams, and the enhanced estates management service and have made a significant contribution to improving these services.

Complaints

An effective complaints scheme is an important component of a culture of continuous improvement. Complaints provide housing organisations with a valuable tool to inform service improvements. Genuine complaints will draw attention to where service delivery is poor, or where problems are occurring. Procedures should be in place to provide evidence that improvements and changes to service have occurred as a consequence of receiving a complaint, and where compensation for inconvenience or distress should be made. Recorded complaints should be part of the evidence base for service review and continuous improvement processes. For a complaints procedure to be effective there must be management information that can be used that determines patterns and trends among groups of tenants.

Sources of advice include:

- The Scottish Public Service Ombudsman at **www.valuingcomplaints.org.uk**
- The Housing Ombudsman Service at **www.ihos.org.uk**
- The Local Government Ombudsman **www.lgo.org.uk** – see specifically publications on dealing with complaints (*Running a complaints system*) and approaches to restitution (*Remedies*)

3.4 Transforming data into information

Collecting customer feedback is not an end in itself. Housing organisations must understand what the information means and use it to plan service improvements, otherwise the service becomes unresponsive.

There is no point collecting data that is not analysed. This, as a minimum, means counts, so that percentages can be provided in order to track trends. But it is more useful to link the satisfaction results to key characteristics of property and tenant. Confidentiality should not be used as a reason not to analyse data in this way. The results can still be presented in a way that protects individual identities. The gain is that, instead of knowing whether overall satisfaction levels are going up or down, the organisation can see the detailed trends by property type, area and customer group. The detail and the general trend need to be looked at together as a way of identifying areas which need better understanding. The statistics are not the whole story, more a route into the important detail.

New technology has transformed the way services can be delivered, exemplified by works scheduling and mobile working (Chapter 4). Now the management of transactions is a combined ordering, recording and analysis system. With this comes an explosion of data that can be used to analyse and improve service data. It has become much easier to analyse the number of jobs by work content, cost and distribution, always provided the detail is being collected. From here it is a short step to graphical techniques such as scatter graphs and mapping which can identify outliers for further analysis. In this way, for example, service users can be clustered to identify exceptional volume or cost by variables like length of tenancy, property type and location.

3.5 Customer insight

In order to deliver a customer focused service it is important for housing organisations to understand the needs and expectations of their customers. This is the basis of customer insight. It helps organisations find alternative ways of delivering services that more accurately reflect customer demand, needs and aspirations. Customer insight is being used by organisations to develop more varied levels of service delivery and menus of service that match individual needs more effectively.

Customer insight involves:

- The capture of data on customer needs, behaviour and characteristics
- The conversion of this data into information that can then be used to improve service performance
- The translation of this information (insight) into outcomes.

Customer insight can be an effective approach to:

- Develop a menu of options and choices
- Inform strategic planning and policy development
- Put customers at the heart of the business, allowing future services to be driven by customers' expectations and needs
- Improve cost efficiency by only delivering services that are needed
- Identify processes or services that are no longer required
- Understand what drives and influences satisfaction levels among different groups of customers
- Understand the needs of more vulnerable groups of customers and those who are traditionally hard to reach
- Ensure customers are involved right from the start in the planning and development of services
- Prioritise resources and service development opportunities
- Recognise the best ways to communicate with customers
- Track changes in demand.

Further information on developing customer insight can be found in *Good Practice Briefing No. 32: Customer Insight* (CIH, 2008)

Summary

- The best repairs and maintenance services are already highly focused on delivering a customer driven service.
- This encompasses traditional resident involvement activities, the development of new approaches such as customer insight, and the provision of greater choice and flexibility of services based around individual need.
- Customers and their needs are not uniform. While a core level of service should be available to all, additional services should be flexible enough to meet the needs of different people.

→

- Understanding what is important to the customer will allow resources to be diverted away from activities that are not valued into providing those that are important.

- Full use should be made of existing frameworks for consultation and involvement, making sure that the feedback is used effectively.

- Involvement should be part of the process, ensuring that the views of customers, staff and contractors can be heard and turned into service improvement.

- Service delivery checks are an important way of monitoring satisfaction. The data must be analysed promptly and reported to staff, contractors and customers on a regular basis.

- Surveys, tenant audits and mystery shopping are all ways of getting a mix of hard and soft data about service quality.

- Complaints provide a valuable opportunity to identify genuine areas of poor performance.

- Collecting data is the first step towards customer insight. Step two converts the data into information, while step three translates the information into outcomes.

CHAPTER 4

RESPONSIVE AND VOID REPAIRS

This chapter looks at some of the important features of a good responsive and void repairs service. There are many ways of delivering a good service, but the desired outcome is that the right repair is done to the tenant's satisfaction at the agreed time and on the first visit. The ingredients vary, but transaction costs need to be low, which means reducing error and eliminating paper; appointments have to be made and kept; the work has to be done well, by trained and motivated multi-skilled operatives; and there needs to be a culture committed to making progressive improvements in service quality.

The starting point for a good responsive service is an approach which:

- Simplifies the process, reducing the number of interfaces and reducing the number of people involved

- Speeds up the process, so that each transaction uses very little time

- Avoids duplication and uses information systems to maximum effect

- Is error free (no re-work costs).

A repeated point in this guide is that there is no single route to success, but the common themes are an appointment system backed by mobile working and scheduling software; a supply chain that has been transformed; and a workforce that is wholly engaged. To achieve high levels of satisfaction the needs of tenants should be properly understood and tenants should be involved in service specification. Research evidence shows that tenants want a service that is tailored to their requirements, and it is at the level of service delivery to individual tenants that quality will be judged. The tenant wants it to be easy to report a repair; they want the work to be done without them having to chase; they want the work to be done by appointment, and for the appointment to be kept. They want the work to be done at the first visit, to be done to a good standard, and for the operative to treat them with respect.

These requirements are largely consistent with those of housing organisations providing the service. In order to run an efficient service the aim is to take a fault report without error, raise the order and get the contractor there at the appointed time to do the work on the first visit. The key to an efficient service is to minimise administrative costs and maximise labour utilisation. This means slick systems and no paper. It also means minimising the volume of responsive repairs. Where possible, work should be switched from responsive to planned. Help should be offered so that tenants can help themselves. Ways should be found to reduce the demand made on the service by heavy users. Achieving these objectives is a combination of fundamental service review, good data, continuous improvement, investment in systems and staff training.

Delivering excellence

The Audit Commission sets out the following descriptors in relation to responsive repairs. An excellent housing organisation should:

- Get the necessary work done quickly and efficiently without long-winded approval systems.
- Complete repairs to a high standard within its target timescales, generally at the first visit.
- Use an innovative mix of caretaker, handyperson and multi-trade working to complete repair works in a responsive and customer-focused way.
- Regularly inspect communal areas, jointly with residents' representatives, and ensures the necessary repairs are carried out within target timescales.

Audit Commission KLOE: *Landlord services: Stock Investment and Asset Management* (2004)

4.1 Managing the delivery of the service

Housing organisations have to specify the standards for the responsive repairs service, make sure it provides value for money and is on course to deliver any agreed efficiency savings. How this is done will differ. When the service is provided by external contractors there can be a clear client-side function. The Audit Commission says that factors for successful procurement include actively managing contracts and supplier performance. The role is to:

- Monitor and control all aspects of the relationship between service provider and the customer
- Ensure the contract is delivered at the agreed price and quality standard (AC, 2008:28).

When the service is delivered in-house, the organisational responsibilities can be less clear. A formal client/contractor split can duplicate management costs. If the DSO is performing well there is a weaker case for imposing the costs of independent service monitoring. But where there are service problems the client monitoring function needs to be strengthened. There is no right way; each organisation should work out who does what and be confident that this will produce the required results.

As a starting point, everyone has to share the key objectives. It is not going to work if the DSO is told to deliver decent homes, but is not required to deliver this within budget. The client will set out maintenance targets in terms of:

- Property standards and component specification
- The procurement strategy, in terms of the division of work and overall corporate objectives
- Client and contractor management arrangements
- KPIs for service standards, costs and monitoring arrangements.

The DSO, as with a private contractor, will work within this framework, setting its own procurement strategy for any materials purchasing and sub-contracting, setting and operating its own more detailed targets and monitoring arrangements.

There will be a set of high level indicators of performance, quality and cost which allow continuous monitoring and allow the service to be benchmarked. The high level indicators will be defined by the organisation, but typical ones usually include:

- Speed of response
- Expenditure per dwelling
- Cost per job
- Number of jobs per property
- Material costs as percentage of total costs.

It can get more complicated than this, particularly when trying to establish whether costs like call handling are included or excluded from benchmark comparisons. But the high level indicators are only being used to guide the need for more detailed assessment. It is a matter of challenging the current method of delivery. If the service is being provided by a private contractor it is essential to compare performance with the wider market. If the service is delivered by an in-house team, the question is whether the DSO is providing an exceptional service through a well trained and well managed workforce making a real contribution to corporate business objectives; or is it providing a poor quality service, a high cost service, or a service that is constantly presenting management problems. The high level indicators include the trading surplus as a percentage of turnover, the level of external trading, and more detailed figures such as turnover and material costs per operative. When diagnostic scores show real concerns in these areas (see HC, 2002:8) then there is reason to undertake a complete review of the DSO, or specific key aspects which are cause for particular concern.

4.2 Managing the quality of the service

The quality of the repairs service is crucial. Responsive repairs is the service that most often brings tenants in contact with their housing organisation. The service should therefore pass the test of tenant satisfaction. This must be measured in a variety of ways, including continuous satisfaction surveys and intelligent use of feedback from complaints procedures (see Chapter 3). But a good quality service will meet other criteria such as the standards for:

- Repairs reporting (including out of hours emergencies)
- Response and completion times
- Quality of work
- Completion of the job on the first visit
- Acting quickly when things go wrong
- Customer care.

Achieving high levels of satisfaction does not mean spending more. Getting things right first time is the route to both a better and cheaper service. The aim is to improve the responsive service by taking out complexity, repetition and overlap. Information systems should quickly and accurately identify customers and their history, support the rapid and accurate logging of fault reports, and order work from contractors through linked systems, providing information to everyone on agreed measures of performance.

Getting to this point requires organisations to know about their current costs, where the money is spent, and why it gets spent where it does. It is this knowledge of the existing process that can form the basis of process redesign to achieve efficiencies. The savings need to be verified when looking at buying-in services from external organisations or contractors. It is not a saving if the contractor runs the fault reporting service and the housing organisation pays more for the labour and material costs of repairs. This is simply a transfer of costs. The aim should be to look at the full costs of service provision, admittedly a difficult task when some of the big costs need to be apportioned, but a reasonable estimate is possible and honest approximation is to be preferred over attempts to disguise true costs.

4.3 Reporting a repair

There are two important criteria for customers reporting a repair. First, that the initial contact is easy, helpful and provides relevant information on what will happen next and when it will happen. Second, that this initial contact is the only contact required. Tenants should not have to chase up their repair. They want the contractor to arrive at the appointed time and do the work properly. Housing organisations therefore need a system that collects enough detail to allocate the correct skills to the job, and to give the tenant an appointment.

Accessibility

Tenants must be able to report a fault easily, including outside office hours. There should be a wide and effective range of ways to report repairs including:

- By phone (either through a specialist or generic call centre or central repairs reporting number)
- At housing offices (often including a direct free-phone link to a repairs line)
- In writing
- By e-mail
- Online via the website – which can allow for the use of an online diagnostic tool to aid reporting
- Directly to other staff who are out on estates undertaking other tasks.

When offering different ways of reporting repairs it is important to collect a core set of common data in order to identify the work and assess its priority. Organisations can simplify their processes by agreeing with tenants the preferred method of reporting repairs.

The drive for efficiencies has led some housing organisations to question the value of running local estate or sub-offices. To retain a local and accessible service, options include a local 'presence' or surgery in an existing property or in a 'shop' shared with other service providers. Another approach is to be mobile, like the 'repairs bus' surgeries used not just in some rural areas but by housing organisations such as Brent Housing Partnership and Ealing Homes.

Repairs reporting

Wandsworth Council has introduced an online repairs reporting service for all council tenants. Tenants can access the Council's website and report repairs for their homes, blocks and estates. They can also use the site to view the current status and progress of a repair they have requested. In addition, leaseholders can check the repairs ordered for their block and estate and relate them to the items in their service charge bills.

→

Yorkshire Housing Group has developed simple diagrams to guide the reporting of non-emergency repairs over the internet. They are easy to use and an improvement on plain text. It is also possible for customers whose first language is not English to use this service in one of six different languages.

Homes for Haringey launched a new graphical repairs ordering system (Web GRO) in December 2006, which allows tenants and leaseholders to log repair requests using pictorial guides. Residents simply click on the image of the item that needs to be fixed and then choose an appointment time, including evenings and Saturdays, to suit them. Once the appointment is booked, a reference number is issued to check progress online. By June 2007, over 500 jobs had been logged through this facility. The system does not replace the normal repairs and emergency phone lines but offers another way to report a repair.

Golden Gates Housing set out plans to improve services following a poor Audit Commission inspection result in 2002. The in-house repairs team underwent significant restructuring, modernisation and investment in efficient customer focused IT systems.

As a consequence:

- 100% of repairs are now offered by appointment, including evening and weekend availability and SMS texting confirmation
- Customers are able to report, track and amend their own appointments online
- IT systems now identify and flag customers needs.

In February 2007, Golden Gates achieved a 3 star excellent inspection rating from the Audit Commission.

Diagnostics

There are various software packages that take the tenant through a series of questions leading ultimately to a works order related to a schedule of rate code. There can be issues around incorrect job descriptions which in turn lead to amendments and additional costs. Composite codes are an attempt to compromise: somewhere between precise job orders (which lead to revision) and vague fault reports (which give no measure of commitment or variation).

Northern Counties Housing Association – Service centre

In order that customer service advisers can place a repairs order quickly with the appropriate contractor, NCHA has adopted an 'average order value'. This is based on historical information about the type, number and cost of jobs placed with contractors over the previous three years. The result is an average order value for 80% of the responsive repairs completed over the last year – the common order cost. There is a price ceiling under which all works would be covered by the one average order cost. If contractors receive work over this ceiling figure, they apply for a variation.

Prioritisation

There is a conventional distinction between emergency, urgent and routine, influenced by right-to-repair guidance, with fairly standard targets for response times. Simplicity argues for a small number of priority categories and a good repair service will agree with tenants what work falls into priority categories. A measure of agreement will surround the definition of emergency and urgent work (see NHF, 2004:30-32).

Appointments

The initial logic is to make an appointment when the tenant reports the fault. The tenant knows when the work will be done, and there is no wasted time getting back to the tenant to confirm the arrangements. The difficulty with this is knowing about contractor capacity and grouping work together in a way that makes efficient use of operatives' time. Some housing organisations have therefore left the contractor to contact the tenant directly in order to arrange a mutually convenient time.

The approach chosen should reflect the overall views of tenants. If the general preference is for a fixed appointment when they ring to report the fault, then this requirement has to be translated into a process that works. As tenants will also want an appointment that is kept, this may mean investment in computer systems that can schedule work. If tenants welcome direct contact with the workforce then scheduling can be organised with less system intervention, but may need to be supplemented by better information about the performance of individual operatives.

Out of hours service

All housing organisations must make arrangements for emergency and out-of-hours repairs. This means being able to report an emergency at any time and to have the repair made safe within a target timescale. Methods of achieving this vary, particularly by organisation size and geographical coverage. Local authorities and larger housing associations will usually have some form of out-of-hours call centre. As there are minimum staffing levels, call volume means they are usually linked to other services (for example alarm call) or shared with other users.

Smaller housing organisations will often use their in-house team on a stand-by rota, linked to local suppliers under contract to provide a service. Bigger contractors offer the potential advantages of more in-depth cover, but this is sometimes achieved at the expense of the workforce having to travel long distances.

Whatever the arrangements, emergency repairs are expensive. A call centre should provide as much help and support as possible over the phone to achieve a temporary solution to the problem. This is where manuals, online help and better information about the property can all combine to reduce the need to send an emergency contractor. However, where there is doubt the contractor has to attend.

Housing organisations should monitor the use of the out-of-hours service to make sure it is not being abused (NHF, 2004:40). The work undertaken out-of-hours will usually be to make safe, returning later to complete follow-up work. There will be exceptions, for example, where the full repair can be effected within an agreed time limit, but these must be defined and monitored.

Housing organisations should also monitor the balance between emergency, urgent and routine repairs, gaining more intelligence about the factors driving emergency repairs. Guidance has suggested that emergencies should not exceed 10%, and urgent 20%. Though useful as a starting benchmark, organisations will want to consider trends and to analyse these by client group, time of day, time of year and against seasonal factors such as weather.

Pre-inspections

These should only happen in exceptional circumstances. The aim is to get a fault report with enough information to carry out the work. If this is not possible, in most cases a contractor can arrive and do what is necessary. In effect this is inspect and fix. This leaves the exceptional circumstances where the attending contractor finds the work requirement involves expensive work or significant element replacement. Examples of exceptions might include damp and dry rot. It is these exceptional circumstances where procedures will require special authorisation or attendance by client-side staff.

Pre-inspections should be monitored. Expensive problems may be discovered by accident as a result of gaining access to do responsive repairs. But an organisation with a good asset management policy would expect to reduce the number of accidental discoveries to something approaching zero.

Recharging

Systems should identify work to be recharged so that the tenant is informed at the point of fault reporting, and can then make an informed decision. The problem is less to do with establishing what work should be recharged as about collection. Deciding whether or not to pursue a recharge is not the responsibility of the maintenance team – it is that part of the organisation concerned with income and debt management. Service review should consider the whole process. Tenants should be consulted; the rules agreed; and the collection mechanism established.

4.4 Doing a repair

An effective appointment system usually rests on at least three components:

- Scheduling – to manage resources
- Mobile working – an essential element of scheduling through resource control
- Supply chain – making sure that the vans have the required materials.

When the fault is reported the main aim is to get the clearest possible view of the problem, primarily to get the right skills on-site with the right materials in order to do the repair.

In order to make an appointment at the time the tenant is reporting the fault, information about contractor resources needs to be available. The following sections on scheduling and mobile working expands on this.

Scheduling

Work scheduling has to support:

- Real-time allocation of jobs to an operative's diary
- Route planning and travel optimisation
- Dynamic re-scheduling as new data is received
- A scheduler's view of planned operative proximity when offering appointments
- Capacity to time profile visits to remote areas in order to group appointments.

To achieve this, it may not always be possible to fix operatives' workloads in advance and a more flexible system is required which:

- Dynamically re-schedules based on updates received from operatives about job status
- Recognises that different operatives may take different times to do the same work

- Consistently route plans when re-allocating work
- Always respects the original appointment time and the operative's skills
- Provides visual warnings of potential scheduling conflicts
- Provides options for schedulers to revise appointments, including bringing forward work to keep operatives busy.

How organisations approach this varies. Some use mobile working but allocate all the work for the day; a variant is to allocate all the work but move jobs to someone else if work is backing- up. Either way there is a discipline on operatives to communicate if their job is running late.

Scottish Borders Housing Association – Dynamic scheduling

Scottish Borders is a rural housing association which covers a large geographical area of 1200 square miles, with 85 operatives covering the repairs and maintenance services. SBHA promised its customers a fully appointed repair service, but needed to overcome the challenges presented by the size of the area and fluctuations in demand. SBHA also had a large back log of repairs to address, with a considerable proportion being outsourced to sub contractors at significant cost.

To meet its promise to tenants SBHA:

- Negotiated with operatives to start work from home, saving miles and hours of productive time
- Introduced a dynamic resource scheduling system (Opti-Time)
- Implemented mobile working alongside real time scheduling for maximum productivity and efficiency.

Since implementing the new working arrangements:

- 93% of repairs are appointed, and 98% completed within target
- 30% of the workforce are undertaking programmed improvements and void repairs in addition to responsive repairs
- £250,000 savings have been made on sub contracting
- Repairs backlog has been eliminated
- 25% reduction in installation costs
- Improved tenant satisfaction.

The dynamic appointment system has been so effective that SBHA intends to roll out the programme to include other housing management staff undertaking tenancy visits and void management.

Mobile working

The benefits attributed to mobile working are:

- Maximisation of productive time – no need to start or finish at the depot
- Real-time information about work progress, allowing emergency and urgent jobs to be issued, and stores material items to be restocked
- Routes can be optimised, minimising travel time and giving flexibility to reallocate resources
- Customer feedback and satisfaction can be measured in real time, allowing problems to be dealt with quickly
- Elimination of work tickets and job completions, enabling more accurate and timely data, and therefore better information for those managing the service
- The use of PDAs eliminates all paper other than that needed for legal purposes (e.g. gas safety)
- Integrating the process with the supplier chain removes much of the manual invoice and bill processing activity.

In mobile working a central team controls the flow of work, and the role of the 'planner' or 'dispatcher' is important. Scheduling staff have two responsibilities: to ensure everyone has enough work, and to ensure that every job is done.

The Wrekin Trust – Mobile working

The Wrekin Trust has used mobile working, combining the Opti-Time system with their own software, to improve repairs performance. Results include:
- Most urgent repairs completed in three days
- Time to complete responsive repairs reduced from 30 days to just over 10 days
- Since August 2006, 98% of the 20,000 repairs processes have been done by appointment
- Savings on operative costs estimated as the annual salary equivalent of £400,000 per year.

Repair requests logged with Wrekin's customer contact centre are sent electronically to the Trust's workforce using XDA touch screen handhelds and software designed in-house. The system's advantages include:
- Elimination of paper-based 'work tickets', increasing productive time
- Customer contact details quickly available
- Operatives not distracted by phone calls while working
- Reduction in data capture delays and errors – majority of jobs completed automatically on core system from field captured data
- Elimination of paper chase frees up back-office staff, enabling them to concentrate more on service and team management issues →

- Operatives can take on-the-job photos and videos for information
- Allows closer monitoring and improved control over job prioritisation
- Tenant confirms with electronic signature that the job is completed
- Customer satisfaction monitoring made quicker and easier – immediate job completion information enables staff to telephone straight away to carry out a full satisfaction survey
- One-job-at-a-time for maximum planning flexibility on the day
- Handhelds provide for the recording of materials used in each job which allows for automated van stock replenishment.

Once the operative arrives at the property, the aim is for them to complete the work and move on to the next job. This requires a multi-skilled workforce with vans restocked using mobile data about material used in the course of the last job. One of the interesting challenges is the extent to which scheduling software can link jobs to core competencies, a demanding additional factor when attempting to allocate work in an efficient way.

A measure of efficiency is the average number of completed jobs per operative. The whole aim is to make sure that the workforce can spend the greatest proportion of their time in tenants' homes. The main obstacles are travel, failure to gain access and visits to the builders merchants to pick up materials. Travel costs can be minimised by intelligent scheduling. Appointment systems can work better if tenants are sent a text reminder and offered an incentive to be at home. Stocked vans can help to reduce return visits to those where a specific and specialised spare part is needed.

Text messaging

Wakefield District Housing has introduced an automatic text messaging system (Mobilelogic) which prompts in advance of responsive repairs appointments and gas servicing. Post visit, the system then texts tenants an interactive satisfaction survey which also provides an opportunity for feedback. This enhancement maintains contact with customers and has clear potential to reduce the number of missed appointments or no access situations. Texting recognises changes in how people prefer to communicate. It is relatively low cost and is immediate.

Blackpool Coastal Housing has a text message reminder service for responsive repairs. In the two years before the service was introduced, 'no access' rates ran at between 15% and 19%. Following introduction of the service in December 2004 the figure fell to below 10%. The contractor's time is therefore used more efficiently; repairs staff have fewer calls about missed appointments, and tenants are happier with the service.

Equality and diversity

There are a number of ways in which a responsive repair service can be tailored to ensure that it caters effectively for all customers. Housing organisations should regularly review the systems they have in place to support potential vulnerable tenants and to ensure that these remain relevant and appropriate. In order to do this, the housing organisation should have systems which record data on tenants' special needs and requirements.

Access arrangements for responsive repairs need to accommodate any special needs that a tenant may have. For example, where a tenant is incapacitated, access may need to be organised through relatives or neighbours. Many housing organisations are now following the lead of the utilities companies and making use of password schemes for elderly and vulnerable tenants.

Housing organisations should consider:

- Repairs prioritisation for households with young children, elderly or vulnerable tenants, for example by setting shorter response times for these households

- Routinely treating repairs to the homes of victims of harassment as emergencies

- How information about the repairs service is interpreted or translated for tenants whose first language is not English and how information is made available for those with visual or hearing impairment.

Homes for Haringey – Passport repairs service

Homes for Haringey offers council tenants aged 60 or over or those with a disability an exclusive free online repairs service. The Arms Length Management Organisation, responsible for managing over 20,000 council and leasehold homes in Haringey, has now launched a 'Passport' repairs service.

The picture based repairs reporting system instantly recognises those tenants who qualify and 'passports' them for extra services. The Passport service includes entitlement to non-standard repairs such as a broken shower rail replacement. Additional services include the installation of smoke detectors and repairs and replacement of toilet seats.

Extra services and support are now available for eligible tenants who use the online repairs reporting system, Graphical Repairs Ordering (GRO).

Kier Building Maintenance – Translation cards

Kier provides a repairs and maintenance service to local authorities and registered social landlords across the country. Kier has developed translation cards as a proactive way to communicate with customers for whom English is not their first language. This initiative is in line with Kier's aim of providing a flexible, accessible and sensitive service that is responsive to the needs of individuals and the wider community.

Kier's operatives are required to take translation cards out to all jobs. The translation cards indicate the purpose of the operative's visit, ask the resident to double check the operative's identification card and assure the resident that they do not have to let the operative in if they are not comfortable about doing so.

Translation cards are passed to residents who appear to have difficulty with English prior to the operative entering the property and the resident selects the language they wish to use. Available in the most frequently-used languages of the area, Kier works in partnership with clients and residents to tailor the translation cards to the specific needs of each contract. Operatives are given specific training on how to use translation cards effectively. Once a specific language requirement is identified, the operative is asked to report this back to their supervisor who will ensure that operatives who attend future jobs are adequately prepared.

For further good practice on addressing equality and diversity issues in relation to repairs and maintenance see *Embracing Diversity: A good practice guide* (HouseMark, 2008)

Customer focus

An efficient and effective responsive repair service will go a long way towards achieving overall customer satisfaction with the housing organisation. Doing the work as promised, without the tenant having to chase, and doing it to a good standard, meets the main criticisms many tenants level against their current service. It also means less work for the call centre in terms of fewer calls to chase the work.

Doing the work as promised is easier if the tenant is reminded of the appointment and told that the operative is on the way. Then, if the job cannot be completed on the first visit, they should be told what will happen and kept informed of progress. Not knowing what is happening next is a common cause of complaint.

West Kent Housing Association – Repairs maintenance pact

West Kent worked with tenants to develop a repairs maintenance pact. It sets out the respective responsibilities of the landlord and tenants with the aim of ensuring that they work together to keep homes in good repair. The commitments include:

- Putting tenants' safety first by carrying out gas, electrical and asbestos safety checks on time
- Appointments offered in two-hour slots. Contractors and tenants pay £15 for broken appointments
- Clear standards of works and service delivery
- An agreed Contractors' Code of Conduct
- Tenants leaving their home in good condition when they end a tenancy.

The pact has proved popular and has reduced the number of missed appointments.

(From *What Tenants Want: Report of the Tenant Involvement Commission*, NHF, 2006:41)

For the contractor, doing the job as promised needs to be backed by an exemplary approach to customer service. All contractors should operate under a code of conduct which covers operational and customer care factors such as work on site, complaints, health and safety, accidental damage, confidentiality and security. As a minimum, confirming identity requires an ID card with photograph and date the card expires. It is common for contractors to have a corporate identity including clothing and van signage. Passwords or codes may also be used to aid identification. Wolverhampton Homes, for example, give a job number to tenants when they report a fault, and this job number is confirmed by the operative when they arrive to do the job.

Hunters Hall Housing Co-operative – Repairs code of conduct

In response to tenant feedback, a repairs code of conduct was developed to help tenants understand what to expect from the responsive repairs service. A focus group involving tenants, staff and contractors produced the code, which has been circulated to all tenants and is included in the tenancy pack for new tenants. The code outlines what contractors should and should not do, and also details the Cooperative's and the tenant's responsibilities.

The code of conduct sets the standard for customer care, but the real management challenge is to ensure this happens on the ground all the time. This relies on training and the retention of good and experienced staff. Staff behaviour is key: what the operative does and says will influence what the tenant thinks about the service.

4.5 Post-inspection and monitoring

The extent to which responsive repairs are post-inspected is partly determined by the nature of the contract. The objective should be for the service to be provided by reliable contractors, minimising the need for inspection and using risk assessment to target these inspections in an intelligent way. The use of fixed targets is not efficient. If the contractor is performing well against all key performance indicators, and post-inspection is not revealing problems, the contractor's own quality control measures can be used with greater confidence. If the contractor is performing badly, the client will incur more costs of checking, and under a partnering arrangement might be expected to see these additional client-side costs carried by the contractor.

The basic approach to post-inspection, therefore, is risk based and statistical. This means that some of the basic rules of statistics apply, and that a small organisation may need to inspect a higher proportion of responsive repairs just to have reliable numbers to analyse. However, this is still not an argument for a blanket target. Consider the areas where tenants are least satisfied or where the organisation has its greatest exposure. Housing organisations need to make full use of tenant feedback; it is often counted and reported without being analysed. Having taken the trouble to ask, it is courteous as well as good business sense to look at what is being raised, to act on this, and then to let the tenants know what has happened.

It is important to keep customers informed, especially if there are problems completing the repair. Tenants should be able to track their repair online, so that they know the fault has been recorded, the date of the appointment and therefore when they can expect the work to be done. Beyond this they could be shown how long they have waited for the work to be completed compared with the organisational average, perhaps broken down by type of work and where they live. This will not interest everyone, but will let them know whether their experience is typical, and can support a genuine complaint if they can see that others seem to be enjoying a consistently better service. Similarly, tenants could be presented with comparisons with the service performance of other housing organisations. The comparison must be relevant and credible. It is particularly important that a single measure, such as speed of response, is not identified as the only thing that matters. Cost and satisfaction measures must come into the equation.

Measuring service performance is considered in more detail in Chapter 8.

4.6 Reducing demand for responsive repairs

A variety of approaches have been adopted to reduce the volume of responsive repairs:

- Moving from responsive to planned repairs
- Annual check-up or MOT
- Offering basic home maintenance or decorating skills training for residents
- Extending incentive schemes and support to residents who are able to undertake their own simple repairs
- The use of handypersons or caretakers to carry out basic, non specialised repairs.

Moving from responsive to planned

There has been a general rule of thumb for many years that organisations should aim to achieve a 70:30 expenditure split between planned and responsive repairs. While this is a useful guide, the emphasis is on achieving an optimum balance, placing a responsibility on organisations to understand their costs. From this basis the first step is to do maintenance programmes on a planned basis, rather than in an ad hoc way as part of the responsive budget. There is the possibility of grouping some types of responsive repair together (batched repairs), or of using information systems to look at patterns of failure and intervene on a planned basis.

Drum Housing – Moving from responsive to planned

Drum Housing has experimented with the use of Geographical Information Systems (GIS) to help focus their planned maintenance programme. The idea is to extract, for example, boiler end-of-life data from their asset management system and map the distribution.

By bringing together information from various IT systems about repairs and maintenance hot spots, the association is able to make soundly based decisions about where best to direct the investment made in the housing stock.

Annual tenancy visit

Some housing organisations are reintroducing annual tenancy visits, which can be a valuable source of information. They provide the opportunity to update property attribute records, and to inspect the condition and state of repair of the property, as well as checking tenancy and household information. Annual visits allow organisations to identify unreported repairs (that could become more serious and costly to fix if not dealt with) and also any rechargeable repairs.

Annual visits across the whole stock would stretch the resources of many housing organisations. An alternative is visits triggered by other factors. For example, where there has been no contact with the tenant or no repairs reported for more than twelve month. Or as part of a close-care package or programme to support new tenancies.

MOTs

The Housing Solutions Group (HSG) is a not for profit organisation dedicated to providing affordable and supported homes in the south east of England. Analysis was undertaken to identify general needs properties that are requesting a hugely disproportionate number of repairs per annum, and gain a greater understanding of the reasons behind these demands. This Home MOT initiative entails an annual visit to the top 100 users of the repairs and maintenance service. These households are visited and inspected for outstanding repairs. Whilst on site, the service operative will undertake checks and lubrication of key components. Any repairs identified but not completed during the Home MOT will be booked for a follow-up appointment.

If, after twelve months, the resident has not reported any further repairs and the twelve month property inspection is satisfactory, the resident will be entitled to a no claims bonus payment of £100. This payment will be subject to the following conditions:

* Clear rent account
* Valid gas safety certificate.

In the interests of health and safety, this does not include genuine emergency repairs. Early analysis of the initiative indicate a reduction in repairs of more than 40%.

Melville Housing Association has introduced a *Maintenance Outlook Test* (MOT) with every house being visited every three years so that its condition can be assessed. This allows repairs to be identified and can also contribute to the preparation of long term maintenance plans. A valuable aspect of this visit is the opportunity it gives tenants to raise any concerns they may have with a member of staff.

Tenants' own repairs

Tenants should be given clear information which sets out both tenants' and landlords' rights and responsibilities in relation to repairs. Information should be available in a variety of different places, for example the tenants' handbook, resident magazines, repairs receipts and the organisational web site. This information should reflect tenants' expectations of service, and be combined with help and advice on how to undertake work that is their responsibility.

Hillingdon Homes – Tenants' repairs

Hillingdon Homes used an Innovation into Action grant to establish a Tenants Repair It Yourself (TRY) project. It was set up to explore practical ways of increasing tenants' ability to carry out their repair responsibilities, either by acquiring skills to do the work themselves, or by finding reliable sources of help. Research in four pilot areas identified a range of possible assistance: for those who wanted to do more work themselves, workshops and advice leaflets; for those who were not interested or were unable to do repairs themselves, help to find a contractor or to access a handyperson service for those over sixty (or over fifty with a disability).

The conclusions were that:
- The workshops worked well, and could be extended by modules aimed particularly at new tenants
- Initiatives should complement existing local services and be carefully tailored to need
- The initiatives need to be continually advertised to ensure tenants are aware of the help that is available.

Caretaker and handyperson schemes

Many housing organisations have developed successful caretaker programmes for estates, residential homes and concierge services. They provide a local point of contact and a visible presence, as well as undertaking a variety of practical tasks.

Thurrock Council – Community caretakers

Thurrock Council's community caretakers help to create and maintain clean, attractive estates. Their work includes:
- Clearing litter and arranging the removal of bulky waste items
- Identifying, reporting and, where appropriate, carrying out repairs to communal areas
- Cleaning shared areas and checking lighting and security
- Removing graffiti
- Carrying out simple repairs
- Identifying and reporting unauthorised parking and abandoned vehicles
- Reporting incidents of crime and nuisance
- Patrolling blocks of flats to ensure the health and safety of shared areas, such as stairways
- Assisting older or vulnerable tenants with health and safety measures
- Cutting grassed areas, and treating weeds to keep external areas neat and tidy
- Participating in estate inspections.

Handyperson schemes have operated for home owners for some time, though largely related to older persons' Staying-Put type schemes with limited capacity and uncertain long-term funding (see for example, JRF, 1996). In the public sector they have typically been linked to estate caretaking services, either to help tenants or to reduce the costs of minor repairs. There is little evidence, however, of the adoption on any scale of the caretaking-plus model used in Scandinavia (see PEP, 1997).

Touchstone Heart – Handyperson service

Caretaker or handyperson schemes have been used to undertake simple tasks as a way of reducing the volume of low cost responsive repairs. They have also been used to improve the level of service for vulnerable groups. Touchstone established TLC Services as a domestic and handyperson service for older people, carrying out a range of tasks including help with heavy shopping, cleaning, laundry, minor internal repairs and garden maintenance. TLC employs the staff, some of whom are semi-retired and might originally have been tradesman. Work is done by appointment, and the client pays by the hour, and for any materials used.

The home support service operates in partnership with Age Concern, and is designed to provide access to professional and reliable support services so that older people can retain their independence. It is a positive feature of the service that it is delivered by a local housing association which gives clients a sense of security and safety.

The scheme started as a service to home owners living in the association's retirement schemes in Coventry, but with the support of agencies like Age Concern and Social Services it has been extended to other older homeowners.

Incentive and reward schemes

Some housing organisations have looked at ways in which they can develop reward or loyalty schemes to influence customer behaviour.

Hermitage Housing – Loyalty scheme

Hermitage Housing's customer loyalty scheme (Hermitage Advantage) is designed to offer members an enhanced repairs service. It also benefits the organisation through reduced spend on void properties and improved satisfaction rates for the repairs service.

Elements of the scheme include:
- A faster repairs service with extended hours for appointments
- A 'golden goodbye' for outgoing tenants who leave their property in a good condition
- A free security check, with help to organise recommended work
- Gardening service and handyperson service
- Competitive insurance scheme.

4.7 Adaptations

Organisations differ in where they locate responsibility for adaptations, and the maintenance team may not be involved at all, for example where there is a specialist local authority cross-tenure team. Alternatively, maintenance may be involved with other health and social service specialists in the specification and procurement of equipment and adaptations as part of individual support packages.

There are opportunities for achieving efficiencies and consolidation of expertise through greater volume. First, local authorities with retained stock can consider a cross-tenure service. Partnerships can be extended to include local associations and neighbouring authorities. Joint procurement can identify specialist one-stop services which places responsibility on the contractor to deliver to the agreed standard and the OT's (occupational therapist's) specification of requirements.

It is important to identify a budget as part of the investment plan in order to make the programme explicit and help to focus discussion about the level of required spend. Otherwise there is a danger of relying on patterns of past spending. With knowledge of existing tenant profiles, and an understanding of potential markets, organisations can assess the level of current demand and try to forecast the pattern of demand over the next five to ten years.

In Scotland, Joint Future is the lead policy on joint working between local authorities and the NHS in community care (Scottish Executive, 2000). The aim is to achieve quicker and easier access to a co-ordinated range of services. Because of a focus on supporting people in their homes, there is a link to housing standards and to equipment and adaptations.

There are two further issues that need to be addressed. The first is that budgets are self-limiting because of other resource constraints and that OT skills have been in short supply, and this has acted as a limiter on spending adaptations budgets. The CIH's good practice guide on sheltered and retirement housing (2005c) gives examples of housing organisations overcoming OT shortages in various ways – for example by training in-house staff to assess for very basic adaptations. Self assessment can be used for adaptations like grab-rails. If a tenant says they are needed they can be provided without assessment.

The second comes from organisations that forecast a reduction in adaptation spending after five to ten years on the assumption that the demand will have been met. This assumption is unfounded. The vast majority of existing homes will never be converted to full mobility standards, and certainly not on existing budgets. The work that is done tends to be very specific to the individual resident, and an individual's needs can change and increase over time. There should be a register of adapted property, taking NROSH data items as the starting point, and this information should be available as part of CBL. However, the specific nature of adaptations means that it is often not possible to allocate an adapted home to someone needing those adaptations. An alternative is to consider recycling the equipment and adaptations for use in another home where possible. There will still be costs incurred in tracking, removing and storing components.

4.8 Void properties

CIH's *Good Practice Briefing: Managing voids* (CIH, 2008a) recommends examining the void process in its entirety in order to understand the nature and sequencing of works. It considers the importance of effective communication between departments, contractors and prospective tenants, as well as the allocation of responsibilities and the need for monitoring and progress checking. From a maintenance perspective, measures to improve the process are welcome if it reduces the number of voids occurring or improves utilisation of the notice period and condition of the property on termination.

Delivering excellence

The Audit Commission sets out the following descriptors in relation to void repairs. An excellent housing organisation:

- Has a challenging re-let standard, to which service users have contributed, and which is available to tenants and prospective tenants before they view the property.

- Carries out repairs and safety checks to empty properties quickly and efficiently, to its own re-let standard. As a result, there is a high level of service user satisfaction with the standard at which homes are re-let.

Audit Commission KLOE: *Landlord services: Stock Investment and Asset Management* (2004)

Guidance on voids

- CIH (2008a) *Good Practice Briefing No. 33: Managing voids*
- Communities Scotland (2004b) *Managing housing voids: The impact of low demand properties*

For the housing management team a void represents lost revenue. If it is likely to be difficult to let, it is also a resource that they would like to see improved. While it is void it is at possible threat of vandalism, and may have a negative effect on the surrounding area. For the maintenance team, a void is a perfect opportunity to do work that is difficult to arrange while the property is occupied, for example, work to improve the environmental performance of the property. These views are not necessarily in competition, but it is not always easy to get the balance right.

The management of voids

The decision process for a void starts with an asset management assessment that the property is sustainable. There should be reference to clear guidance on reinvestment criteria when the void is notified, and an option appraisal initiated if required. The process should be sufficiently simple and automated that the appraisal does not add significantly to the void period. If the property is to be re-let, decisions should be based on the amount of work required to re-let the void, with the objective to minimise overall void costs while aiming for a sustainable tenancy (that is, reduce the chances of having to re-let the property again in a few months time). Increasingly organisations are now determining the amount of work to be done prior to letting in consultation with the incoming tenant.

This means that voids are the responsibility of housing management. It is counter-productive to designate a void as 'with maintenance' and therefore not the concern of housing management. Void management can be a complex process, one very open to support from work-flow information systems, but even if the property keys are moving about, the responsibility remains with housing management.

Angus Council – Void turnaround

Angus Council's void procedures ensure that prospective tenants are selected for vacancies within three days of staff receiving a termination of tenancy notice. The prospective tenant can view the property before the outgoing tenant leaves. On the day the property is vacated the new tenant will sign for the tenancy and gain access immediately if there are no extensive repairs to be carried out. A significant number of properties are re-let on the day they become vacant. Overall, 40% of properties are let within two weeks of becoming vacant.

Voids and Energy Performance Certificates

In England all social housing lettings will require an Energy Performance Certificate (EPC) from October 2008. An EPC will remain valid for ten years and can be re-used as often as required during this period. However, where a landlord has improved the energy efficiency of the dwelling, they will most likely commission a new certificate, to supersede an existing one. The certificate uses the familiar white goods' A-G band labelling system to display the energy and environmental impact rating of the property, and lists cost-effective energy improvement measures. Housing organisations will need to plan and budget to meet this requirement, and to ensure the void process is not delayed. Many housing organisations will lack the level of data needed for an EPC at letting, and the way this data is collected needs to be agreed as part of the process. Only an accredited Domestic Energy Assessor (DEA) can produce an EPC. This means that if the work is carried out in-house, staff will need accreditation. Whilst data can be collated by a non-accredited person, the DEA will need to be satisfied about accuracy before the EPC can be issued. If the work is contracted out it might be linked to a full stock condition survey.

- Interim guidance can be found in *Energy Performance Certificates: Interim Guidance for Housing Associations* (Housing Corporation, 2007d) **www.esd.co.uk/has/Good_Practice_Interim_Guidance_HAs.pdf**

- For general information see Energy Efficiency Partnership for Homes, 2008, *A Landlord's Guide to Energy Performance Certificates*. Available from: **www.eeph.org.uk/partnership/index.cfm?mode=view&category_id=24**

- A sample EPC and up-to-date guidance are available from **www.communities. gov.uk/documents/planningandbuilding/pdf/319282**

Planning for voids

Housing organisations will have a series of strategies to support void planning, including reducing voids through achieving sustainable tenancies. From a works perspective, anything that improves the ability to forecast void work will enable contractors to plan their work more effectively and thereby help to reduce the void period. While some circumstances, such as eviction, abandonment and the death of a tenant all demand more complex responses from housing management, the aim is to manage routine end of tenancies by encouraging tenants to follow their tenancy agreement and give proper and full notice of termination. Various schemes have been adopted that encourage tenants to return their keys on an agreed date, and with the property in good repair.

Sovereign Housing Association – Cash incentive

When tenants move out they can claim a £200 bonus if they:
- Give four weeks notice
- Have no arrears
- Allow viewing by prospective tenants
- Leave their property clean and safe.

Void budgeting

Organisations should look at void costs as a combination of income and expenditure: of rent loss and void works. Having a budget for a void property then allows a trade-off between works costs and rent loss.

The decision process requires a minimum agreed letting standard and a budget-related authorisation procedure for making decisions where there may be a requirement for major works. The lettings standard should be published and based on discussion with tenants and ideally with prospective tenants.

Void works

The agreed works to a void property will certainly include safety checks and any necessary cleaning. There will be circumstances where the tenant has left possessions in the property. The voids procedure should outline what needs to happen with possessions and take account of informed consent under the Mental Capacity Act 2005. Before acting, housing organisations should be clear about the legal position in relation to tenancy termination due to death or a move into a care home where any next of kin will be involved.

It is common practice for housing organisations to use a contractor with specialist void teams, partly for the spread of skills, but also to isolate the work from other calls on resources. This approach is by no means universal; for smaller organisations or more isolated properties a general contractor will be used, possibly one doing responsive repairs. However, this requires an agreed prioritisation of resources between void works and responsive repairs to ensure void management is not disrupted.

Northern Counties Housing Association – Property care teams

NCHA's review of costs identified disproportionate sums spent on the clearing, cleaning and minor repair activities to void properties. It was agreed that semi-skilled operatives could carry out this work to improve quality and value for money.

The association now has nine Property Care Teams. Their remit has extended from void work to wider estate management tasks such as minor external repairs and the removal of graffiti.

Whatever the approach, the practical difficulty is that there will be peaks and troughs in workload. Balancing the amount of work done before void and after letting can help achieve a more even volume of work.

Works after lettings

Some housing organisations prioritise re-letting the property, and arrange for further works to be done once the tenants have moved in. Depending on the type of work it is perhaps not quite so efficient for the contractor, but the rent (or possibly a discounted rent) is being collected, the work can be planned, and the tenant can have a say in what is done.

Inspection

While post-inspection of responsive repairs should be statistical and risk-based, the voids inspection process should start from the assumption that they are all inspected. There are capacity issues here, and a maintenance inspection should not delay the re-let, but the quality of handover should be assessed, and combined with the opportunity to update the stock condition database.

Monitoring

The amount of work done at void should be monitored in the light of responsive repairs in the following six months or so. This is to establish whether there is any evidence that new tenancies are resulting in more fault reports, and if so, whether there is a pattern in terms of type of work or, indeed, type of tenant. There are two evidence streams to be considered, both dependent on good data and information systems.

First, evidence of re-work. Are there void works which are failing and resulting in calls on the responsive service? There is an argument that this is work under a form of void warranty, and should be part of the performance measures for the void contractor.

Second, are there responsive repairs being reported in the first six months that might have been avoided if the work had been done when the property was void? This is about the level of predictable failures. If there is a boiler in the property that is of a type and age that means others are being replaced, it might be cost effective to replace it when the property is void. Other items might result in changes to the void specification. It may not be cost effective to replace tap washers in order to avoid a future responsive repair, but it probably makes sense to check for dripping taps, leaking ball valves and damaged window ironmongery.

Summary

- Reporting a fault should be simple and accessible to all.

- Priorities should be agreed with tenants.

- Arrangements for emergency repairs should seek to minimise volume.

- Appointments should be made for non-emergency works, and the success for the systems will depend on knowledge of capacity and control of resources.

- Text message reminders to tenants about appointments have been found effective.

- The whole process should be simple and cohesive, eliminating waste, paper copies and administrative time.

- Works scheduling and mobile working are areas to consider to improve efficiency and service performance.

- The operative arriving to do the job should be multi-skilled and properly equipped. This should be backed by commitment to delivering the best possible customer care.

- Minimise client-side costs of post-inspection. Target areas of risk, for example contractors or trades performing poorly, or where complaints are highest. Co-ordinate with the contractor's post-inspection programme. Use residents to monitor the contractor's performance.

- Service quality should be continuously monitored, and used with information from the complaints procedure to improve the quality of the service.

- The demand for adaptations should be assessed and included in the budget forecast.

- Voids need to be turned-round quickly. The re-let period can be minimised by encouraging tenants to give proper notice and carrying out works while the property is tenanted.

- Responsibility for managing voids should rest in one place.

- Undertake a pre-void inspection to assess the works required and inspect as soon as the keys are returned.

- Void security means, as a minimum, making lock changes, leaving curtains, maintaining the grounds and making routine external checks.

- The void standard should be agreed with tenants. Distinguishing pre- and post-letting repairs can help to reduce the void period.

- Works done while a property is void should be monitored for evidence of re-work and patterns of future fault reporting that could be eliminated.

CHAPTER 5

PLANNED MAINTENANCE

Planned maintenance programmes need to be well managed and deliver value for money. The first part of this chapter looks at the strategic issues and how long term objectives are realised in detailed works programmes. The second part then considers the implementation of planned programmes, the position of leaseholders and the delivery of cyclical programmes.

5.1 The nature of planned works

Planned maintenance covers cyclical and improvement works and programmed renewals. Detailed programmes should be established on a three to five year rolling programme of works that have been discussed with tenants and align with business objectives. Then the work must be procured on the best possible terms and delivered in a way that achieves high levels of tenant satisfaction. Cyclical maintenance is work undertaken on a specified cycle such as servicing and cyclical painting, and fire alarm and fire equipment checks. These are not capital works, but have similarities to other planned works in terms of procurement and contract management. For the purpose of this guide improvements generally refer to the installation of components that have not previously been part of the fabric, such as the first time installation of central heating or insulation. Programmed renewals (or future major works) are the planned replacement of components that are judged to need renewal. This includes carrying out interim repairs that will postpone the need for replacement, an approach known as Just In Time (JIT) or Intelligent Programming. Works are planned on an assessment of the relative cost and risk of doing the work now against doing work at some point in the future.

Decisions about repair or replacement are judgements that require guidance about the amount of repair that can be done before replacement is the preferred option. These protocols should be transparent, fair, easy to understand, affordable and agreed with residents. Factors to be considered are condition, the target standard, the cost of repair, and the age of the component (as an indicator of future costs or a reflection of social obsolescence). Backing these should be good information systems that indicate areas of cost increase. For example, if there is a trend of roof and gutter works in a particular street or estate, it may indicate that the economics of group replacement should be considered.

A move towards JIT means potential failures have to be identified, based on data and modifying factors (original workmanship and specification, tenant usage, local circumstances, environment and exposure). Then decisions have to be made about what is replaced, doing this as part of an assessment of the risks of not doing the work.

5.2 Programme management

Managing the work

Some organisations regard planned maintenance as contract management and link it to the development team. This is seen to encourage shared specifications, but may mean it is harder to achieve a co-ordinated approach with responsive repairs. Others run their planned and cyclical operation as part of a maintenance team that includes responsive repairs. This views stock management as a core function of housing management, with the planned programme under the direct control of those responsible for letting and managing the existing stock. Such an approach offers a reasonable chance of co-ordinating repair and planned programmes, reflecting the priorities of investment programmes, while ensuring that housing services have access to technical skills when acting as client in procurement or programme delivery.

Prioritising work

The starting point for delivering a planned programme is defining what work needs to be done to which properties. Tenant consultation is central to this, while contractors should have an input to the sequence and phasing of the work. The starting point, however, for a first draft programme, is the investment plan. This is covered in more detail in the following chapter on asset management.

The investment plan should be based on stock condition data in an asset management database. The data is likely to be drawn from a combination of surveys and works programmes. The costs need to be available at unit level so that analysis can be undertaken by any grouping of properties. The resulting agreed investment requirement is then translated into a five year rolling planned programme as the basis for budgeting and procurement.

The database provides the initial guide to the work that needs to be done, and pre-inspection confirms the actual situation on the ground. The database must be maintained by capturing the works that have been done, and just as important the works that have not been done (because they were delayed, or refused, or there was no access). All this requires careful management of the data cycle:

- planned programme first-cut
- inspection
- confirmed programme
- works done.

The first cut of the data identifies properties for programmes of pre-inspection before moving to the detail of address-specific contracts. This requires a policy framework which is clear about how work is packaged. There are two basic approaches. First, whole house or external/internal, often delivered on an area basis. Second, element programmes, which can also be area based. Whole house internal improvements might look attractive, but they may be more disruptive, and might involve premature replacement.

Estate-based external, internal and whole house programmes have been the conventional approach because of the economies associated with site set-up costs and the practicalities of consultation and tenant liaison. They were easy to understand, and tenants could see how they worked. But, given past patterns of investment and the fragmented pattern of ownership on estates, it seems likely that in the future there will be more interest in just-in-time planning, which makes greater demands on information systems and on tenant consultation.

With non-area programmes, particularly for internal work, it is important to look at whether a common specification and volume programme will give the required cost savings. The rules about what work gets done must be fair, easy to understand, affordable and agreed with residents. Non-area programmes also need different plans for consultation with tenants and leaseholders. It may reduce the estate-level consultation with tenants, being more concerned with the individual tenant, but if leaseholder works turn out to be smaller scale but more frequent, this could increase the amount of time devoted to consultation.

Shaping the programme

Residents should be involved in the preparation of investment programmes. This can happen at various levels, from high level priorities through to influence or control of area budgets. As a result the organisation should be able to announce firm plans well in advance, keep residents properly informed and to co-ordinate work with the responsive and cyclical programmes. Working on annual programmes is not good enough. The minimum requirement is for a published programme which rolls out at least six months in advance, but this must be underpinned by detailed work with a longer time horizon.

All this is consistent with effective procurement and good communication. It means making financial commitments over financial years and helps avoid situations where plans could be set back by a lack of money. Public announcements must be linked to budget guarantees, based on the best possible control over programme planning, budgets and procurement.

In addition to an involvement in agreeing programme priorities, residents should be involved in the specification of components. This should extend beyond choice over colour and style to issues of usability. It is for example important to take account of residents' views about whether items like taps, boilers and radiator controls are easy to use.

Staffordshire Housing Association – Kitchen replacement programme

Following a competitive tendering process, Staffordshire appointed a kitchen supplier on the basis of the following factors:

- Kitchen range
- Customer service
- Cost
- Continuity of supply.

Working with customers, the supplier then produced a bespoke design for each type of kitchen within pre-determined guidelines. Under the new kitchen replacement programme:

- When a customer's home is surveyed for kitchen replacement, the customer chooses their worktops, doors, handles, flooring and wall tiles
- This information is then transferred electronically to all individual contractors involved, reducing the need for separate visits to the property
- Each customer receives written information including the start date, the expected duration of work and what the installation process will involve
- A dedicated project officer liaises with residents on progress throughout.

Tenants have a dedicated kitchen fitting team, customer satisfaction is over 99%, and the association has the benefit of fixed pricing and confidence in quality.

Resident liaison

The steps in programme delivery include establishing which properties are part of the contract, what work is to be done, and the sequence in which the work is to be carried out. This involves discussion with residents collectively and individually, and can be done by the client, the contractor or a combination of both.

Anything that adds clarity and involves communication has value in terms of delivering planned programmes. This usually involves a combination of resident meetings and discussions with individuals. Buses have been used as both a mobile office and display space. The complexities of decent homes works and asbestos removal have both been targeted using DVDs.

The roles and responsibilities for liaison must be clearly established. If the contractor is paid to do the liaison, the client's role is to make sure this function is done as specified. The client must not run a parallel liaison service to cover the shortcomings of the contractor. If the liaison role is carried out by the client, the contractor needs to be involved to take the maximum advantage of their experience in project planning so that the works are delivered efficiently. Residents need clear information about the arrangements, so that they know who is responsible and how to complain if things go wrong.

5.3 Leaseholders

In England and Wales flats are owned and managed under a leasehold system, while in Scotland the ownership of flats is usually governed by the provisions of the title deed for the property. Flat ownership in Scotland has been a significant feature of housing management for many years, as has leasehold management for a relatively small number of local authorities. The management of leasehold stock is growing in significance and future mixed tenure schemes will increase this further.

Despite the legal differences, the requirement in Scotland, England and Wales is for effective arrangements for consulting, advising and recovering allowable costs for repairs, improvements and communal services. The delivery of this service is an overhead which must be considered, particularly by those with substantial leasehold development programmes. Information systems have to properly identify and apportion costs. Investment plans should be modelled for individual schemes so that leaseholders can see future costs and additional resources have to be set aside for consultation, liaison and cost recovery.

Housing organisations need to ensure:

- Collection and management of good quality data about what services are provided and the way the charge is apportioned. Housing organisations must have accurate information about the terms of individual leases as different versions may have been used over time even within an individual scheme

- Delivery of a good quality service, which is well managed and able to demonstrate that costs have been reasonably incurred

- Good communication with leaseholders to keep them informed and consulted. Within a block or scheme, consultation on works programmes should include leaseholders as well as tenants. The potential for disagreement has to be recognised and managed, as leaseholders will have to pay for their share of the costs

- Timely and accurate information about costs and charges due, with audited annual accounts.

Leasehold management and service charge recovery requires housing organisations to develop detailed procedures for consultation, charging and accounting. In England and Wales the freeholder is responsible for repairs to the structure of the property and any common areas, but leaseholders may have to pay some or all of the costs involved. Most service charges are now variable, based on the actual or estimated cost of the service. The power to levy a service charge and the leaseholder's obligation to pay it are governed by the provisions of the lease. The freeholder must consult leaseholders before carrying out works over a certain value, and will need to give careful consideration to the implications of non-traditional forms of procurement such as partnering.

While sinking funds are a condition of grant funding for housing associations in England they are not usual in the local authority sector. However, they can be set up if the lease provides for it, (HQN, 2006) and they can help spread the costs of capital repairs so that leaseholders do not face sudden large bills. In England the Audit Commission's KLOE relating to leasehold management looks at whether housing organisations have made sound and consistent decisions about the use of sinking or reserve funds.

Further guidance

- CIH (2003) *Leasehold management: A good practice guide*
- NHF (2005) *Service charges: A guide for housing associations*
- HQN (2006) *Leasehold: Sinking/reserve funds and KLOE 12*
- Audit Commission (KLOE) *Management of leasehold and shared ownership housing*
- Leasehold Advisory Service – **www.lease-advice.org**

5.4 Cyclical programmes

The term cyclical is conventionally used to refer to pre-paint and paint programmes and annual gas safety checks. It is extended here to include servicing programmes such as fire equipment checks and lift servicing – programmes that may be part of service charges. Housing organisations must be able to view the whole range of programmes if service charges are to be properly calculated and managed. As with other areas of data management, this means that costs have to be linked to the relevant units (in the case of service charges, almost always through their parent block). Once set up, the data must be maintained.

This data can then support planning, managing and monitoring programmes. The range and relative complexity of these activities mean that data needs to be widely available within the organisation, and should be accessible to tenants and leaseholders as well, following the same pattern as information about responsive repairs performance. When housing staff visit a scheme they should know when the fire alarms were last checked or when the grass should have been cut.

In areas of cyclical work, other than safety checks which are prescribed, residents can play a central role in defining priorities and monitoring performance; there are real opportunities to work together. Housing organisations will not want to undertake cyclical works on a rigid schedule irrespective of need and residents will understand that sometimes works can be postponed, provided there is some control over area budgets which means that something else is prioritised instead. This ability to invest in estate improvement is central to the delivery of places where people want to live, and doing this helps achieve the social organisation's goals in terms of the sustainability of their assets.

William Sutton Trust – Joint reviews

William Sutton has sixteen local joint committees of tenants and staff, known as estate management committees. These are usually chaired by a tenant and are focused on influencing and monitoring local service delivery. Recent successes include securing changes to a local authority street cleaning service and traffic control measures. They also run summer play schemes bringing together children from their estate and wider neighbourhood.

Pre-paint and paint programmes

Pre-paint and paint programmes have traditionally been undertaken on a five year cycle or similar, and are procured and managed like other planned programmes. There is the same scope for efficiency gains through collective procurement to achieve larger volumes of work.

The merit of a regular cycle is the commitment to be aware of and address problems that might be causing tenants' concern, and to do preventative work before greater expense is incurred. However, there is no need for a rigid cycle of pre-determined works. The judgements are about doing work in a timely manner. Housing organisations should undertake inspection on an approximately five year cycle, but the work might be delayed for a year or two, and work on other properties brought forward. Managing this emphasises that data about works undertaken need to be attributed back to individual properties or blocks.

Gas safety checks

All landlords have a legal duty to carry out annual safety checks on all gas appliances. Failure to comply can lead to a criminal prosecution. The essential requirements are:

- An annual safety check on all gas appliances by a CORGI registered installer
- A record of each safety check kept for a minimum of two years
- A copy of the safety check to be issued to the existing tenant within 28 days, and to any incoming tenant at the start of their tenancy
- All reasonable steps must be taken to achieve access to carry out gas safety checks
- Good records must be kept of the need for inspection and the status of each individual property, with action and timescales
- An agreed policy of escalation to achieve access, including last resort legal action
- Legal options include the use of injunctions requiring the occupier to allow access; possession proceedings (suspended in return for allowing access); and local authorities can evoke Section 81 of the Environmental Protection Act 1990 (magistrate warrant allowing forcible entry for inspection and disconnection)
- An independent check on the inspection team to ensure the work has been carried out correctly.

Delivering excellence

The Audit Commission sets out the following descriptors in relation to gas serving. An excellent housing organisation should:

- Annually service and carry out safety checks to all internal gas appliances and carries out all necessary repairs and replacements promptly.
- Use innovative ways to gain access where service users refuse it, using forced entry as a last resort and only after taking appropriate legal advice.

Audit Commission KLOE: *Landlord services: Stock Investment and Asset Management* (2004)

South Staffordshire Housing Association – Whole system approach

South Staffordshire's whole-system approach to gas safety centres on a full partnering agreement for gas servicing, installations and maintenance. The agreement includes a fixed price for both the maintenance and repair of installations and enables close working with the contractor.

One of the results of the partnership arrangement is the introduction of a system called Notifi. This allows tenants to access the service schedule, and enables the engineer to update the schedule via mobile phone. The system has increased access rates, with over 90% properties accessed on the first call.

Access is the main problem in achieving inspection. All housing organisations must have information systems to monitor progress and demonstrate compliance. The best of these are linked to asset management databases to maintain detailed records, using work flow systems to manage the access process. This will issue follow-up letters, and then trigger action by housing management, with court proceedings if necessary as the last resort.

Brent Housing Partnership – Gas servicing

BHP has implemented a live web based system for running and monitoring its gas servicing programme. Contractors share the system and jobs are allocated to engineers via PC tablets. Information available to contractors includes programmed appointments, letters to be sent, a count down to certificate expiry and a list of vulnerable tenants.

A ten-week countdown to the annual visit is in place to allow BHP and its contractors to send a total of six letters, including two hand delivered, reminding tenants of their responsibilities and offering appointments including Saturdays. They also make a reminder home visit on Saturdays, speak to residents and liaise with housing officers to contact named relatives on the tenancy agreement forms in the hope of achieving a positive result before court action is needed.

Tenants are regularly reminded of their obligations to allow the visit through articles in the council's borough-wide magazine; BHP's newsletter for tenants and leaseholders; a health and safety leaflet is sent as part of the reminder procedure and posters are put up in the communal walkways of all tower blocks. Tenants can also request an appointment through BHP's website.

There is debate about whether gas service and gas safety checks should be done together. In looking at this, a useful first question is what additional work is done for a service compared with a safety check, and how much extra this costs when a qualified person is already on site. The additional work usually surrounds the distribution system, and organisations need to consider whether servicing leads to maintenance savings. In value management work, Liverpool Housing Trust (LHT) introduced a water sampling regime with processes for cleaning systems and adding corrosion inhibitor. Performance was improved by increasing boiler life.

Further guidance

- CIH housing manual **www.cih.org/housing manual** – chapter on repairs and maintenance, section on gas servicing, safety and repair

- SFHA (2005) *Housing associations duties as landlords: Procedures for access to undertake annual gas safety inspections* SFHA Good Practice Guide

- Communities Scotland (2006c) *Gas Safety Matters*

- Audit Commission (2005a) *Gas safety guidance for landlords*

- For further information about the LHT value management work see the Centre for Construction Innovation website **www.ccinw.com/images/demos/003LHT.pdf**

Solid fuel, oil and electrics

Gas appliances are covered by specific legislation. While other forms of domestic energy are not part of this legislation, there are good reasons for including them within inspection programmes.

Solid fuel and oil appliances are causes of fatalities through carbon monoxide. Solid fuel appliance testing and ambient air monitoring should be included in annual servicing programmes. And oil fuel boilers should be checked once a year just like gas appliances. A policy of installing carbon monoxide detectors should include both solid fuel and oil appliances as well as gas.

In addition to Portable Appliance Testing (PAT), conformance to Institute of Electrical Engineers (IEE, 16th Edition) suggests a periodic inspection report (PIR) at a maximum ten year interval for domestic property. Housing organisations should regard this as the upper limit, and should also undertake a test when the property is re-let. The recommended maximum testing regime for emergency lighting is three years, with one year for fire alarms, and this could be considered an indicative standard for PIRs in common areas.

Other plant and mechanical systems

This equipment must be carefully recorded so that those who need to know can see:

- the servicing schedule
- who is responsible for initiating a service
- carrying out the work
- managing the quality of the work.

Water systems should be assessed under the code of practice for Legionnaires disease (**www.hse.gov.uk**). Items like lifts, fire alarms, door entry and community alarm systems need to be maintained in accordance with manufacturers' guidance. Items like fire alarms and fire protection equipment might be included under a consolidated service contract. But whether it is one contract or many, relevant people need to know who is responsible for systems in any particular scheme, and to be able to access this information quickly and easily.

Landscape and other ongoing maintenance

The routine work content of landscape maintenance has to be specified for each block or scheme. While there has to be some timetable flexibility to allow for the vagaries of the weather, the intended outline programme should be available for all, so that any deviation from the schedule can be identified and followed up. The management of these contracts, together with cleaning and other servicing issues, is an area where many housing organisations have found tenant involvement delivers considerable benefits.

Periodic attention is also required to landscaped areas, the pruning of trees and replanting of older shrubbery. This might form a component of landscape maintenance contracts, involving an element of annual improvements as well as periodic maintenance. Some work may fall into the category of required, to minimise risk, while other work might be desirable but not urgent. The programme should be agreed with residents and the costs properly apportioned so that service charge costs can be calculated.

Saxon Weald Homes – Geographical Information Systems

Saxon Weald Homes uses a geographical information system (GIS) to help improve the management of grounds maintenance contracts and the calculation of service charges for general needs tenants, tenants in retirement housing and leaseholders. It has allowed the organisation to break down the overall cost of the grounds maintenance contract, capture the area that needs attention, allocate the correct classification to it, and therefore establish the contractor's cost. This gives the client far better control over quotations for work.

Grounds maintenance is an estate service item and can be paid for through a service charge. However, leaseholders are not liable for payment unless the service is set out in a schedule to their lease.

Summary

- The overall investment spend should be defined by the asset management strategy. This is the spend that can be funded under the business plan.

- Though it may not be fully funded, the investment plan should have been based on an assessment of the work needed on the stock.

- The asset management strategy will also set out the broad framework for programme delivery in-line with the procurement strategy. This will include the way works are packaged by component or groups of components.

- Planned maintenance includes interim repairs to postpone major investment. Housing organisations should define and support the assumptions that drive repair/replacement decisions.

- The detailed programme should be agreed through a process of analysis pre-works inspection and consultation which will take into account the priorities of tenants and housing management and the views of partners about the efficient delivery of programmes.

- Work needs to be prioritised in support of the business plan. It needs to be procured to provide value for money.

- The housing quality agenda identifies the worst property for attention, but these should be assessed before they are included in any programme.

- The proposed programme should be developed and agreed to provide a rolling programme. The old cycle of planning related to the annual budget process is not appropriate.

- The planned programme should not be used to cover possible over-spends in other areas; this results in cautious budgets and last minute demands to spend money.

- Contractors must demonstrate the capacity to deliver what is planned.

- Clients must monitor and manage contractors. The role is to keep control of performance, costs and quality.

- Tenant feedback from satisfaction surveys and the complaints procedure should be used to improve the service. Tenant involvement has been found to be very effective in areas of common area and estate maintenance.

→

- The management of leasehold stock is growing in significance and housing organisations should review their approach to service charges, and consider the implications for consultation and the additional requirements for information systems.

- Paint programmes can move off rigid cycles of pre-determined works.

- Gas servicing requires good systems and a closely managed process, and these should be applied to other areas of cyclical maintenance.

CHAPTER 6

ASSET MANAGEMENT

This chapter looks at asset management in its strategic context, particularly in relation to the organisation's business plan. It focuses on three key elements of an asset management strategy: investment planning and the stock data needed to provide cost forecasts; target standards informing investment plans; and portfolio performance and approaches to measurement and option appraisal.

6.1 Asset management strategies

In the previous chapter on planned maintenance the starting point for prioritising work was the investment plan. This plan is one of the outputs from an asset management strategy. It takes a broad view of current and future housing need and the delivery of commitments in the business plan. The asset management strategy is therefore the framework within which repair and maintenance operates. There is no standard formula, but most asset management strategies will:

- Set out an investment plan that is affordable and achieves agreed standards
- Establish a process for determining investment priorities in support of business priorities
- Define the principles of procurement and the approach to be adopted to maximise the value of planned programmes and reduce the call on responsive repairs.

The asset management strategy must ensure that the business can afford the investment requirement in its business plan, and establish the steps it needs to take to align the objectives of growth, product and service strategies, with target rates of return for a re-structured portfolio delivered through new development, acquisition and re-investment.

The asset management strategy will not usually go into detail about procurement strategies or service delivery plans, but it will state the terms of reference under which these related strategies and plans will operate.

Asset management strategies should be evidence based, take account of tenant views, be part of a wider set of integrated strategies, and informed by an understanding of patterns of demand, regeneration, sustainability and community development (see for example WAG, 2002; Housing Corporation, 2003:3).

In organisational terms, asset management can be part of planned maintenance or under the control of a director responsible for housing services, strategic planning or business growth.

Detailed information about strategic asset management can be found elsewhere (for example NHF, 2004b). The themes covered in this chapter are concerned with the key elements of the strategy: investment planning, target standards and the measurement of portfolio performance.

Useful guidance on all aspects of asset management can be found on the Housing Forum: Constructing Excellence website. The Housing Forum have developed an asset management process toolkit – which can found at **www.constructingexcellence.org.uk/tools/gamptoolkit/process.jsp**. It covers areas such as Stock Condition Surveys, Options Appraisal and Property Asset Management Planning

---

6.2 Investment planning

An effective repairs and maintenance service will be underpinned by an investment plan. The important elements of an investment plan are:

- Planned maintenance forecasts based on evidence from a stock condition database, and driven by a schedule of rates which reflects local prices. The forecast should specify whether or not contractors' fees, preliminaries and VAT have been included
- A forecast that is adjusted regularly to reflect the results of decisions about stock retention and option appraisal
- Life cycle assumptions based on national standards but adjusted for local experience
- Costed to achieve a defined aspirational standard which reflects tenants' priorities
- Non-survey costs (responsive, void, cyclical) informed by past budgets
- The costs and assumptions reviewed and if necessary revised or rephased to align the investment plan with the business plan and with tenants' priorities.

In the context of other documents the investment plan should reflect the asset management strategy and inform the business plan, as shown in the following diagram:

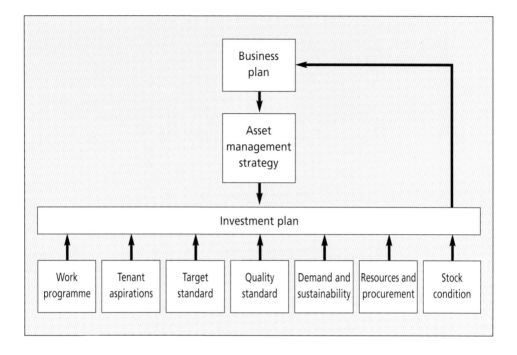

The output from the thirty year investment plan, revised annually and preferably as a formal input to the budget process, provides the context for overall investment priorities as well as the framework for a detailed five year planned maintenance programme that, as an initial minimum, demonstrates the delivery of the relevant housing quality standard.

Preparing a robust investment plan requires reliable and comprehensive stock condition data held in a suitably integrated asset management information system.

Stock condition data

The investment plan relies on up-to-date stock condition survey data, and there is a need for comprehensive and reliable coverage. Housing organisations spend a considerable proportion of their income on maintenance, and it is reasonable to allocate a proportion of this spend on the intelligent planning of this work. Housing organisations should consider a budget of about 1% of their total maintenance spend to cover data collection, data management and data analysis. The important points to bear in mind are:

Samples

- A sample survey is for strategic purposes. The results will be cloned or extrapolated to give information about the whole stock. The sample size depends on a variety of factors but is generally not less than 10%, and should include 100% of all blocks.
- Statistical reliability is the first requirement, and for this reason housing organisations should aim for 100% surveys of acquired or street property, particularly where these are very dispersed and heterogeneous.
- Aim to do as large a sample as possible because sample surveys have severe limitations for detailed planned programmes, and cannot identify un-surveyed non-decent property by address. Moving towards effective 100% real data is necessary if the database is to go beyond strategic planning to support planned programmes, portfolio scoring and option appraisal.

Collecting data

- The data collected in a condition survey should be no more detailed than is required for operational planning purposes. Sufficient information is needed to provide the basis for well-informed pre-works surveys. Beyond this, databases have to be maintained, and the simpler the data the better the chance that data is good quality.
- The data should be sufficient to inform reporting and delivery of target and aspirational housing quality standards, and to report on energy efficiency. It is also an opportunity to collect attributes that inform other processes – for example property information for NROSH (National Register of Social Landlords) and CBL (choice based lettings). However, the list can quickly become unwieldy, and it is important to focus on what is required and known to be useful.
- Invasive testing is not part of stock condition survey methodology, and this means that collecting data about asbestos and structural works are separate and specialist activities.
- The condition of specialist M&E (mechanical and electrical) equipment such as lifts and other plant is usually beyond the scope of a stock condition survey. However, plant items can be recorded as attributes in the stock condition database, and provision for maintenance and renewal costs should always be included in the investment plan from relevant specialist sources.
- In England and Wales housing organisations must collect HHSRS data as part of their stock condition survey. There is no requirement to undertake full HHSRS surveys at the standard required for enforcement action. Surveys should include the most common hazards such as heat, cold, fire and trip hazards.
- The scope of the survey should include all assets for which the organisation has a repairing responsibility. This includes any leasehold property, non-housing assets and any estate management costs such as unadopted roads, underground drainage, external lighting and play areas.

Energy data

- A stock survey is an opportunity to collect energy data. The minimum requirement is to provide an indication of SAP (Standard Assessment Procedure) scores across the stock, and where data is comprehensive and reliable can be used to support affordable warmth strategies.

- The introduction of Energy Performance Certificates means that housing organisations have to decide on the benefits of carrying out RDSAP (Reduced Data SAP) as part of the stock survey. Energy Performance Certificates will be required for all re-lets in England from October 2008, and housing organisations should look at the way the process can be streamlined through the routine collection of relevant data for EPCs (Energy Performance Certificates) and EcoHomes XB.

Guidance on stock condition surveys

- DETR (2000a) *Collecting, managing and using housing stock information* (3 volumes) **www.communities.gov.uk/decenthomes**

- NHF (2002) *Stock condition surveys: A guide for registered social landlords*

- *The Housing Forum Gateways in the Asset Management Process Toolkit* provides information and checklists in relation to stock condition surveys. These can be found at **www.constructingexcellence.org.uk/tools/gamptoolkit/ stockconditionsurvey.jsp**

Data management

While the stock condition survey is a starting point, mature databases are the product of data from a variety of sources, primarily from rolling surveys and works programmes.

Rolling surveys are a continuous programme of surveys designed to visit unsurveyed properties and to ensure that data more than about five years old has been re-checked. There are various approaches. One is an internal and external programme on a five year basis. A variant is to have a cycle of external inspections to inform the cyclical programme, and a separate programme of internal inspection.

In theory every visit to a property is an opportunity to check data quality. With handheld technology and training, housing management staff can make a cost-effective contribution to the improvement of stock data.

Works programmes are the other main source of updates. The coding for works ordering should map to the stock condition database and interfaces are needed from contract management, through invoice payment back to the stock condition database.

Condition is not the only change affecting the database. Database management should also take account of stock changes. If the stock condition database has interfaces with the housing management system the essential gains and losses will be properly reflected in the stock condition database. For organisations with a significant development programme it is important to model the new stock based on component life cycle assumptions common to the rest of the portfolio. If development scheme appraisal makes contrary assumptions the differences should be reconciled.

Quality control – it is important to audit stock databases to assess their quality against the reality on the ground. The audit should show the level of divergence, suggest ways of correcting systematic errors, and propose action to fill gaps in under-represented stock.

Information systems

Specialist asset management packages are concerned with the expenditure side of asset management. They hold attribute and condition data against the stock and can forecast costs based on schedules of rates and life cycles. The best can offer much more functionality based around this for the planning and management of investment programmes. But at their core is a knowledge of physical assets. An asset management strategy that is concerned with measuring the performance of its stock, based on current performance and future patterns of demand, needs to combine internal data on income and expenditure (including management costs) with external data on market trends and organisational views about priorities. This should be informed by the views of current tenants and the potential needs of future clients.

For larger organisations there is a range of software which provides the functionality to forecast investment requirements and undertake modelling to examine the effects of re-phasing programmes of work. These packages have various modules for the management of planned programmes, to record the location and condition of asbestos, and the management of gas safety checks.

Asset management software needs to be linked with housing management systems. These should co-operate in a seamless fashion so that relevant information is available to those who need to know. Housing organisations looking for asset management software should consider putting integration on a par with functionality and price as evaluation criteria.

Many smaller housing organisations tend to lack asset management software because of cost and lack of specialist resources, even though they would benefit from the functionality. For these organisations in particular, the growth of web enabled software might encourage the growth of application service providers (CIH, 2005:52).

Free stock condition software (HCOND) has been developed for the Housing Corporation by UWE. It is designed specifically for the use of small housing associations. A link can be found **http://environment.uwe.ac.uk/hcond/**

6.3 Target standards

Social housing, as a product, must meet minimum standards, respond to the needs and aspiration of the market, and be aligned with the service being provided. Investment plans must be prepared in the knowledge of the housing product on offer, and the way this needs to be modified in line with a changing or developing market.

The applicable housing quality standard (Communities Scotland, 2004; CLG, 2006; WAG, 2002a) is the benchmark. Beyond this housing organisations usually choose to define their own target standard reflecting the views and aspirations of their tenants and perhaps prospective tenants.

In defining the aspirational standard, housing organisations will take into account the requirements of households in greatest need and the way investment can improve the quality of life in local communities. They should also position the portfolio for longer term changes to patterns of demand and area preferences, to achieve low running costs, to be environmentally sound and to provide a desirable place to live. Outside the home this embraces wider concerns about the local environment and the management of open space. Inside the home affordable warmth criteria will be a key element, with insulation and efficient heating systems being top of the agenda.

Asset management needs to operate in the context of clear corporate product, service and access strategies. While aspirational property standards can be set in isolation, it is better to consider first the target markets (both current and new markets); how those markets are addressed (product, services and access); and how this is segmented by market or area. One consequence of this is that there may not be a single, uniform standard across the organisation's stock, but one driven by differing customer requirements.

Environmental sustainability

Asset management strategies need to take environmental sustainability into account. While it is important that development programmes deliver high standards, it is the existing stock that will dominate the carbon profile for many years. There are currently no mandatory standards relating to the environmental performance of the existing stock. Housing providers can draw on EcoHomes XB, a self-assessment method to identify the environmental performance of their existing stock (Sustainable Homes, 2007). XB was developed by the Building Research Establishment (BRE) and is supported by the Housing Corporation. Whilst this is not mandatory, it is promoted as good practice and supported by the Corporation through guidance and training. There are no set targets which need to be achieved, as was the case with EcoHomes (now replaced by the Code for Sustainable Homes). It provides organisations with a baseline from which targets to improve environmental performance can be derived. In the context of climate change, future-proofing the stock becomes more and more important, as some of the extreme weather events seen in the last few years start to become more common. Landlords will have to think of measures to deal with issues such as flooding, overheating and water shortages. It is therefore important that climate change considerations are a central part of any asset management strategy for existing stock, as well as being a key factor in developing new homes. Given concerns about the environmental performance of the existing stock, a housing organisation's asset management strategy should:

- Identify the poorly performing or at-risk stock against agreed sustainability criteria. These criteria might include energy performance, environmental impact and potential risks such as flooding or overheating

- Forecast the costs associated with works to improve thermal efficiency and reduce carbon emission

- As part of option appraisal, identify the parts of the stock that perform poorly and have high forecast improvement costs.

The forecast additional costs must be fundable by the business plan, requiring careful modelling of options in the investment plan as part of a risk assessment, taking into account the impact of different levels of investment on future demand and resulting income streams.

Environmental sustainability

- The Energy Saving Trust provide information and free advice on energy efficiency measures to housing providers: **www.energysavingtrust.org.uk/ housingbuildings/localauthorities/**

- General information on improving the environmental performance of existing properties can be found at **www.greenstreet.org.uk**

- Case studies on sustainable refurbishment can be found at **www.sustainablehomes.co.uk/pdf/GPGRefurbs.pdf**

- Guidance and information on EcoHomes XB can be found at **www.bre.co.uk/ecohomes**. See also *Ecohomes XB: A Good Practice Guide* at **www.housingcorp.gov.uk/upload/pdf/EcoHomes-XB.pdf**

- A Sustainable Housing Design Guide for Scotland (2007) is available at **www.communitiesscotland.gov.uk** (together with a web-based Sustainable Development Policy Wizard).

Green design

e²S, a subsidiary of Black Country Housing Group provides environmental consultancy services to social landlords, local authorities, designers, engineers, cost consultants and manufacturers. It also undertakes surveys, develops general and detailed designs, presents physical and virtual models and monitors actual performance. e2S has pioneered a 'green' design process which can be applied to any project on any site. Fore more information see **www.bcha.co.uk/homes/ sustainable.html**

Development and maintenance

There should be a common product specification that informs development activity. Maintenance and development teams should work closely together to share customer feedback and the experience of maintenance cost-in-use.

Under existing arrangements compromises are usually made in order to get schemes built. This does not mean that shared goals are unachievable, and there are two areas which can be given particular attention. First, new development should start from an agreed specification of key components such as heating systems, windows and doors, with a common set of assumptions about costs and life cycles. If the specification then has to be varied, an informed view can be taken about the implications and, if necessary, the additional costs built into the future maintenance plan.

Second, common standards need to be looked at in the context of mixed tenure and affordable housing. Development partners are offering a product designed to attract home buyers. There are positive aspects to this, but it may mean that housing organisations are inheriting future unfunded maintenance liabilities. It is therefore important to ensure that projected maintenance can be afforded in the long term while looking at whether equivalent standards can be delivered to other tenants.

6.4 Portfolio performance

Performance analysis and option appraisal are central to asset management. There are various ways of measuring portfolio performance, but whatever method is used it must be possible to answer a simple question: has portfolio performance improved? Poorly performing assets have to be identified and returns improved. The options are re-investment, disposal, or development to support the product strategy. The mechanisms for analysis are those of portfolio scoring, option appraisal and neighbourhood planning.

Housing organisations have to match their stock portfolio to business objectives, and planned programmes must support restructuring of the portfolio in line with business criteria. There is a need to identify problem stock and manage these units either as sustainable assets or as stock for disposal. Investment plans have to be based on agreed need and spending priorities. The key aspects of measurement are to identify under-performing stock and areas of emerging need. This requires more information about the performance of the existing portfolio, the costs of meeting aspirational standards and the current and future demand for property of a particular type in a particular area.

For advice on option appraisal and neighbourhood sustainability see *Housing Investment Appraisal* (NHF, 2004b)

The asset management issues for supported housing are covered in the above NHF publication. For further advice on risk, see *Risk Management Toolkit for Supported Housing* (Housing Corporation and Tribal Group, 2005)

Portfolio scoring

There is no single approach to portfolio scoring, the methodology being heavily dependent on the nature of the stock and the size of the organisation. The thinking began with so-called 'traffic light' measurement of existing stock performance, a widely used and simple way of identifying homes needing more detailed option appraisal before deciding about re-investment. There are numerous examples of simple assessments. See for example, Larkin (2000) and NHF (2004b). Factors considered include turnover, void levels, environment, socio-economic indicators such as unemployment and educational achievement, community wellbeing and stability.

There are now more sophisticated methods of weighting the required return in a net present value (NPV) approach taking residual valuation into account. This methodology is capable of factoring in other measures such as quality, dispersal, housing need, preferred partner status and corporate objectives.

Scoring can be based on available data, but more sophisticated approaches require the ability to make longitudinal assessments. Valid comparisons of performance over time need a stable set of performance indicators and a solid database. Organisations should aim to:

- Collect fine-grained data on management costs
- Code maintenance costs from planned, responsive and cyclical works
- Separately identify leasehold costs

- Have available forecasts of future rent income at unit level
- Be able to calculate net rent income (rent collectable less write-offs)
- Measure void periods
- Store valuations, ideally at the level of individual dwellings
- Capture internal data on patterns of demand
- Link customer satisfaction data back to property characteristics
- Hold more robust data on tenant characteristics.

This may take time to achieve, and housing organisations should start with what is available and build from there.

Option appraisal

Option appraisal in the social housing sector is not just a financial equation; it has to take social factors into account. A scheme may produce a poor return on financial criteria, but meet housing needs that are viewed as being central to the delivery of its business objectives. The important point is that this decision to invest is made explicit.

The principles of option appraisal are well established. It is likely that basing the approach on NPV (Net Present Value) will attract support because this is a common method of looking at relative return. It also means agreeing the period of the forecast, whether residual valuation should be taken into account, and if so, the method of valuation. There are also questions to be considered about the treatment of interest charges, and whether development cost assumptions are consistent with cost and life cycle assumption used for the existing stock.

The challenge is to devise a framework for option appraisal that supports the asset management strategy. Crucially, the decision to reinvest in stock at a detailed neighbourhood, scheme or asset level should be a judgement that balances financial criteria against a housing management assessment of the need for investment and the wider business priorities. The methodology must be embedded in the decision-making process. The modelling is not intended to make decisions, simply to support the decision-making process. If it is to do this, the modelling needs to be relatively simple but command confidence. Spreadsheet models are widely employed to look at the options. Sensitivity analysis is quite common, but it is much rarer to find risk modelling.

Neighbourhood planning

Neighbourhood plans can operate as a vehicle for adopting a more co-ordinated approach to regeneration, particularly in areas of low demand or high turnover.

Again there are various approaches, but there are some common themes:

- Investment decisions should be linked to a view about housing need in the area
- Investment should be linked to wider initiatives, whether this is housing management or the co-ordination of activities associated with neighbourhood regeneration
- This provides a very effective platform for the involvement of tenants in the development of priorities, and can be given continued substance through the operation of ring-fenced local area budgets. One option is to localise management services, giving local residents a clearer idea of the trade-offs involved in using available resources (Hills, 2007:174).

Kirklees Neighbourhood Housing – Estate planning

Kirklees has a well-developed and co-ordinated approach to ensuring that priorities for investment in homes and estate environments take account of tenants' and residents' views. The focus is on estate plans, which encompass both short-term and long-term visions for local areas, aiming to ensure each area is popular and well-managed. An estate plan is a working document, frequently updated and refined to reflect changing circumstances and any new information.

Estate plans are informed by:

- Estate manifestos – drawn up by KNH in conjunction with tenants' and residents' associations (TRAs) on a 3-year cycle
- Annual investment conference – open to all tenants
- Estate walkabouts – an opportunity to focus on smaller scale environmental concerns
- Tenant-led budgets – 4 local tenant committees determine how local environmental budgets of £250,000 are spent in their area
- TRA meetings and local area forums – both ensure that residents' views and discussions feed into the broader planning of investment and services
- Street contacts – an opportunity for individuals not involved in TRA's to feed in views from 10-15 neighbouring households.

A key role of neighbourhood planning is to identify properties that are at risk of low demand and to prepare action plans to deal with them before they become financial liabilities. If the stock can achieve target standards at reasonable cost, the business plan should provide for co-ordinated re-investment that includes environmental works to secure the long term future of the area. Proposals for disposal should be reviewed in terms of the impact on the local community.

Neighbourhood asset management plans provide a basis for a more co-ordinated approach to asset management, and particularly to recognising that investment planning should not be undertaken in isolation from housing management. The approach gives considerable weight to housing management priorities rather than being dominated by re-investment and development concerns. The options to be considered look at different approaches to the management and use of the stock, and are not limited to decisions about stock improvement.

Summary

- Housing organisations must have an asset management strategy.
- Investment plans must be based on up-to-date data and an awareness of future demand.
- Resources must be targeted in relation to the business plan.
- Plans must be based on solid analysis delivered by excellent information systems.
- The aspirational stock standard should be agreed and shown to be fundable.
- Housing organisations should have an affordable warmth and fuel poverty strategy, either as a part of the asset management strategy, or as a separate document.
- Boards should require a portfolio strategy that identifies priorities for growth, re-investment and disposal.
- Stock performance can be assessed through scoring, option appraisal and neighbourhood planning.
- Option appraisal is an important element of asset management, and should be an integral part of the way the maintenance service operates. It represents wasted time and effort if the organisation is not looking at options but at a foregone conclusion.

CHAPTER 7

DELIVERING THE SERVICE

Social housing in Britain is estimated to spend between £6 and £10 billion a year on responsive and planned maintenance. It is therefore an obvious target for savings, which need to be found without loss of service quality. This chapter looks at the way repairs and maintenance services are delivered. Housing organisations are expected to have a strategy which addresses modern methods of procurement such as partnering. This approach makes new demands on the client. The role of the contractor becomes more important as a professional resource in an integrated team. The benefits of volume are explored through collective procurement and the opportunity for other forms of collaborative working. Finally the objectives of partnering are reviewed.

7.1 Procurement strategy

Procurement is the process of purchasing goods and services from third parties. The national agenda is set in terms of the Latham (1994) and Egan (1998) reports, developed through Constructing Excellence by the Housing Forum and the Movement for Innovation (M4i). The aim is to move some procurement from competitive tendering towards longer-term relationships based on 'open book' methods of accounting that set out clear measures of performance and look for sustained improvements in quality, efficiency and customer involvement.

In England the Audit Commission (2004) expects organisations to look for significant cost savings and quality improvements through standardisation, partnering down the chain and discounts for longer contract periods. The expectation of the Scottish Executive is that RSLs will deliver better value for money and a better quality product through a more collaborative approach between clients and the construction team (Communities Scotland, 2006d:7).

Procurement advice

- Advice for board members is provided in a self assessment framework for procurement (Housing Corporation, 2003c)

- In Scotland, good practice in procurement is required under Performance Standards (Communities Scotland et al, 2006a), and advisory guidance set out in *Procurement guide for use by registered social landlords* Communities Scotland (2006d). See also *Assessing Performance* at **www.scottishhousingregulator. gov.uk**

- In England and Wales, Audit Commission (2004; 2008); Welsh Audit Office (2005); and the guidance section of **www.idea.gov.uk**. following the link to procurement. See also IDeA (2006) and Housing Corporation (2006c).

- The NHF (2007) has published a revised *Guide to EU procurement rules*

- The Office of Government Commerce has advice at **www.ogc.gov.uk**, following the link to procurement, where details of the Gateway Process can be found.

- The OGC also has advice on eAuctions at **www.ogc.uk/index.asp?docid=1001034**

All housing organisations should have a strategy for procurement which complies with EU directives, national law and standing orders. The procurement strategy will provide the framework for making decisions about the purchase of materials and services, and will seek to do this in a way that delivers efficiency gains.

Maintenance procurement must have outcome targets related to the organisation's corporate and business plan objectives: for example, to deliver a programme of building services and works so that tenants are living in good quality, safe, well maintained and easy to heat homes in sustainable communities. The aim is to find the best way to deliver a service which achieves corporate and service objectives, meets tenants' needs and aspirations, the needs of local communities, and continuously improves quality and efficiency.

The procurement strategy must then set out a way to deliver this programme economically, efficiently and to an agreed standard that is capable of being measured.

The principles of a procurement strategy are:

- Obtaining the right materials, services and works at a good price

- Negotiation with suppliers to achieve maximum savings

- Development of long-term partnerships provided this is consistent with good performance and value for money – defined as 'the optimum combination of whole life cost and quality necessary to meet requirements' (HAIAF, 2006a).

Procurement should contribute to an organisation's corporate objectives, which is why principles such as consultation and involvement should be established as part of an asset management strategy. It is here that housing organisations can define the way their service is to work.

It is also appropriate to consider the options for delivering works in a way which offers wider benefits of employment and skill training for local people. A procurement strategy in isolation may not see the value of local employment objectives. The case for this has to be established at a more strategic level.

There can be issues around local labour clauses which are unlawful and breach EU procurement directives. There are however examples of community benefit being part of partnering agreements, and a JRF report (2002) discusses ways in which this can be achieved.

Use of local labour

In Westminster, the partnering strategy of **CityWest Homes** encourages contractors to employ local labour. This has been reinforced by a local Public Services Agreement with Westminster City Council setting targets for the training and employment of young people in construction.

Willow Park Housing Trust (Manchester) has ensured that its work to regenerate the area and improve local services has also provided employment opportunities for local people: 35% of its staff are also tenants. Local people are employed across the organisation in housing management, neighbourhood wardens, customer services and in-house repairs teams. (*What tenants want: report of the tenant involvement commission* NHF, 2006).

Family Mosaic – Social enterprise

Family Mosaic established a social enterprise company, Resico, to employ its own tenants, particularly those on benefits, to deliver a range of services including:

- Cleaning services to other landlords and private sector clients
- Telephone based surveys, for example to monitor satisfaction with repair works
- Provision of temporary staff
- Decorating
- Building maintenance.

Homes for Islington and Kier – Youth training

Since embarking on its building maintenance and repair partnership with Kier, Homes For Islington's (HFI) Audit Commission rating has improved from 1 to 2 stars. Kier attributes much of this improvement to the tenants having direct input into how they want the service delivered and to the unique training scheme for local young people which has proven to be so successful it is now being rolled out nationally.

The First Start youth training initiative was developed from an idea that arose through tenant consultation, when a couple of tenants from the Market Estate in Islington painted a gloomy picture of life for young people once the school day ended.

This meeting inspired the development of the First Start training programme that would give real skills to local young people, through the renovation of an empty property under the supervision of Kier staff.

Trainees for the First Start programme are put forward by various referring agencies – including Connexions, schools and the local Youth Offending Team – and each year the places on the programme have been over-subscribed.

Launched in 2003 with funding from the Learning and Skills Council, First Start has so far seen 38 trainees complete the programme in Islington alone, each of them gaining valuable skills in areas such as carpentry, plumbing, electrical work, health and safety, tiling and planning. On completion participants receive a certificate and professional reference for their achievements. It has proved to be an excellent way of helping them build a career, with many trainees going on to apprenticeships in the building trade.

The scheme has been rolled out across a number of other authorities, including Brighton and Hove City Council, Greenwich Council, Ealing Homes and Ascham Homes, and in 2007 the scheme won a National Training Award.

Equality and diversity in procurement

The CRE (now part of the EHRC) set out the following expectations in relation to equality and diversity and procurement activities:

- All contracts are delivered in a way which is non-discriminatory, and promotes equality of opportunity for staff, the general public and businesses
- The goods, works and services provided by contractors cater for all users' needs
- There is no difference in the satisfaction rates of users, or staff, from different racial groups

- Contractors are representative of the local population, or of the area from which the businesses are drawn, with respect to ethnic diversity
- Contractors work on a voluntary basis to promote equality of opportunity beyond the scope of the contract.

Organisations need to carry out a review of their procurement activities to make sure that they encompass equality of opportunity principles. A CRE report on Race Equality and Procurement in Local Government (2003a) suggests a number of questions to ask when conducting a review:

- What are your procurement objectives? Are they primarily related to cost savings? Do the objectives include promoting race equality? If so, what effect has this had on current practice?
- How does your procurement practice affect different racial groups, directly or indirectly – as providers of goods, works or services; employees (your own as well as those working for the contractors); and users of the goods, works and services you provide?
- Is there evidence that your procurement policies or practice affect some racial groups adversely?
- To what extent have you built race equality considerations into each stage of the procurement process?
- Does the procurement process include consultations with residents, staff, businesses, and other organisations from all sections of the community you serve?
- Is the impact on race equality different for different types of procurement, from spot purchasing to private finance initiative contracts?
- Are there differences between council departments in the importance they place on race equality? Do some departments put more emphasis on it than others? Is race equality given more consideration when procurement is managed centrally?

For further good practice on addressing equality and diversity issues in relation to procurement see *Embracing Diversity: A good practice guide* (HouseMark, 2008).

7.2 Procurement options

There are a variety of options available to housing organisations in delivering repairs and maintenance. The following summary is drawn from Better buys: Improving housing association procurement practice (Audit Commission, 2008:20-21).

Repairs and maintenance provision	Description	Advantages	Disadvantages
In house	Service is provided and managed internally. Internal processes are tested against quality standards, benchmarks, and/or the market.	Long-term relationship. Integrated systems. VAT exempt.	May not be competitive with the market.
External	Service is provided by one or more contractors and managed under traditional contract arrangements. Performance is measured against targets set in the contract.	Competitive market. Easy to find expertise. Responsibilities are clearly defined in the contract.	Dispute can be difficult and disruptive. Us and them mentality can develop. Using a high number of contractors increases the number of invoices. Liable for VAT.
Mix of in-house/ external	A combination of internal and external provision (see above).	Best of both worlds approach. Reacting to the market.	List of preferred contractors can be unwieldy. Difficult to develop long-term relationships.
Partnership through groups/consortia	Housing associations group together to create economies of scale, share services and/or expertise.	Bigger influence in the market. Shared experiences. Utilising skills of others.	Time intensive. Difficulties in agreeing specification. One member may dominate.
Partnership with private sector	A development on traditional contracts where a relationship is built between the client and contractor. Partnerships may include open-book accounting, co-location and shared risk.	Encourages an honest, open relationship. Innovation in delivery. Additional community and environmental targets can be achieved through partnership.	Management can be resource intensive. Benefits can take time to materialise. Long term partnerships could be uncompetitive with the market.

In their report the Audit Commission made the following recommendations:

- Identify gaps in procurement skills and take steps to fill those gaps either by building in-house capacity or seeking external expertise
- Identify and collect information on the market before considering procurement options and ensure that performance monitoring and benchmarking is undertaken as part of the procurement cycle
- Consider and evaluate all models of collaboration for achieving greater efficiency, including shared services in groups and consortia
- Explore and evaluate a greater role of e-procurement tools
- Ensure that residents are involved in, and have appropriate opportunities to influence, relevant procurement processes.

Although the recommendations were aimed at housing association general procurement practices, they have relevance for any housing organisation concerned with repairs and maintenance procurement.

7.3 The integrated team

The importance of procurement skills has been emphasised. While this chapter is mainly concerned with different methods of procurement such as partnering, the Audit Commission (2008) concluded that the key factors determining a successful approach to procurement relate primarily to internal organisational capacity and culture. The research, which was of housing association procurement, found that well managed organisations, with the appropriate skills and knowledge, are more likely to improve services and release efficiencies regardless of their structures or methods.

The client function

Repairs and maintenance contracts must be managed. The task varies depending on the nature and scope of the contract. There is always the need to ensure the service is delivering what has been specified. In the past a good client would specify requirements, then confirm that the service was meeting the terms of the contract, report on contract performance and ensure conformance to the code of conduct (a document setting out the required standards of workmanship, behaviour and probity for all contractors and service providers). Now the role is less autocratic and more team-based, but not at the expense of professional judgement or rigor. In managing a collaborative or partnership style of approach the client needs:

- The ability to communicate business objectives. This starts with an understanding of customer requirements; seeing how a given quality of service can be delivered at lower price without compromising cost-in-use; and the ability to influence and network to secure the support of key people.

- Knowledge of procurement. The Gershon Review (2004) was highly critical of the lack of professional skills in the public sector. The procurement strategy must be prepared and managed by a professional team with the right skills and experience to deliver efficiencies and service gains.

- The creation of an effective working environment. If services are to be delivered in partnership, the culture of partnering must be driven from the top, with commitment, so that the philosophy is embraced by all those involved in delivering the service. People can be instructed to show trust and commitment, but they need to be convinced.

- Getting core values to run through the process. Delivering repairs and maintenance is a team game: good performance in the board room has to be matched or bettered on the ground. Customer satisfaction will be boosted if the values of trust and commitment are part of the everyday attitudes of the people working in tenants' homes. That means a continuous programme of training to deliver service quality.

- Motivation through winning. An effective team needs people to be convinced. This can take time, but it helps if people believe they are part of something that works. It means creating a climate of shared objectives; an ability to measure performance easily and without ambiguity; to identify and resolve disagreements quickly; and to ensure a focus on immediate remedies and improvements which can be measured and can command very broad support.

The **Housing Forum** (2000) defines the successful client in the following terms:
- Commits themselves to leading and supporting the collaborative approach
- Spends time at the beginning of the project planning and preparing and defining what they want
- Makes sure they appoint the right people and teams
- Clarifies objectives and priorities – time, cost and quality
- Consults, involves and satisfies their customers
- Seeks value for money and takes whole life costs into account
- Works with the team to understand the risks involved in the project and makes provision for them
- Considers performance incentives for the team
- Encourages trust and promotes empowered teams
- Insists on transparency
- Ensures systems are in place to minimise the potential for contractual disputes and provides methods of quick problem resolution when all else fails
- Regularly measures, manages, evaluates and reviews performance to foster continuous improvement.

The client must ensure that the contractor understands exactly what the housing organisation is trying to do and be committed to achieving this. This is true whether it is an external contractor or an internal team, and whether it is a collaborative style partnership arrangement or a traditional form of contract. There is the need for leadership rather than simple management. It is not just about setting and meeting targets, agreeing policies and defining procedures. There has to be room for vision, for a view of what the service could be like, the potential for change and the opportunity for this to happen.

Beyond the vision, there needs to be a contract or form of agreement to specify the rules, agreed measures of what is being achieved, and incentives to deliver the improvements. The contract must start with a clear understanding of what the organisation wants to deliver by way of a service. It has to offer continuity to encourage commitment to continuous improvement, and include inbuilt incentives to reward innovation, efficiency, quality of service and product and cost economies. It should seek to minimise but not ignore the need for dispute resolution and termination.

The client's role in managing the contract means a focus on product quality, service efficiency and service quality. Time and resources have to be available to make this happen. The requirement is for the right kind of resources: an understanding of business needs, combined with contractual and technical knowledge. Performance has to be monitored and emerging issues have to be dealt with before they become problems. Managers of the contract must know how to measure what has worked well and what has been less successful, and to do this using data from the contractor, from tenants and the client's own independent measures of performance.

For further guidance on the client role, see Constructing Excellence (2002) *Rethinking the construction client* at **www.constructingexcellence.org.uk**

The contractor function

In the past, responsive repairs and void works were almost always managed in-house, with the works undertaken either by a DSO or one or more external contractors, usually, though not always, under some form of term contract. Planned maintenance was usually tendered, but some in-house teams had the capacity to bid for larger or more specialist work. The recent trend has been to reduce the number of contractors, to move towards partnering, and in the process to stream-line or reduce the client-side role. This has seen the contractor undertaking some of the tasks previously carried out by the client: for example, running the responsive repairs call centre or the tenant liaison function of planned programmes.

A review of process should consider the best way to achieve scale, simplicity and expertise through a variety of service delivery arrangements including group structures, joint ventures, partnerships with other associations, and partnering with contractors. The objective should be to look for a process that minimises interfaces by creating better integration of the service delivery team.

Responsive repairs is an area that has been particularly affected by changes in the contractor's role. Whatever the organisational arrangements, the process from fault reporting to invoicing should be cohesive and seamless. Putting the call centre and contractor together (co-location) has been seen as one approach, with merits from a maintenance perspective, but at the expense of a one-stop customer experience as far as tenants are concerned. Some organisations have gone beyond co-location and passed the whole activity on to the contractor. This does not remove interfaces, it simply shifts them. If all the fault reporting and work management activities are handled by the contractor, these systems should be integrated. But information has to be passed from and to the client, and the specification of these requirements has to be given careful consideration. The client needs detailed information on works and performance. The contractor needs up-to-date information on tenure and asbestos, and ideally any information related to the special needs of the tenant or access to the property.

Individual organisations will asses the risks differently. The arguments for a packaged service include co-location as a way of minimising communication difficulties. This can be achieved through the contractor's call centre while avoiding direct set-up and staff costs and with the potential for scale efficiencies. If repairs and maintenance is outsourced, whether to a DSO or an external agent, the kind of questions that arise are about first point of contact service, fixed costs, and the long-term integrity of service data:

- What are the costs and benefits of first point of contact being with the external or internal contractor against a specialist or generic service provided in-house?
- What are the contractor's fixed costs? Do any of these duplicate irreducible in-house costs, and what mechanisms are there to reduce these contractor fixed costs in the future?
- What mechanisms are in place to ensure that detailed service data is returned to the housing organisation to support asset management and analysis of trends in service use?

An outsourced approach does not always fit well with the way an organisation wants to deliver services to its tenants. Customer care may be seen as an integrated service, or there may be concern about control over the service provided by an external or internal contractor. If these risks are thought to argue for in-house delivery, then the questions are:

- Can the organisation run a good call centre? Can it operate on a scale which delivers the required level of customer care, can opening hours be long enough to meet access criteria, and can the staff be adequately trained and managed?
- Can an appointment system be operated in full knowledge of contractor capacity? The client's involvement in the process adds to the complexity of systems integration
- Can fault reports be delivered to the contractor seamlessly, without paper, and with enough information to avoid criticism that the work is wrongly specified? This is a major interface, where costs are incurred and errors made. Where the responsibility is on the contractor, the failure to capture a correct fault report is a cost borne by the contractor.

It is stressed throughout this guide that there is no single approach to the efficient delivery of repairs and maintenance. The whole operation of responsive repairs can be outsourced to a contractor and this can work very well. But it is not the solution for all organisations.

If fault reporting and ordering remains a client function it is essential that works orders are generated without paper; a simple efficiency that should now be exploited by all but the very smallest housing organisations. There are also efficiencies on invoice and payment, but these need to be thought through in the context of standing orders and payment procedures.

7.4 Collective procurement

The Gershon Report (2004) identified the potential for efficiency gains through collective procurement, and this has led to the emergence of national and regional procurement consortia. The idea is that purchasers combine to procure an agreed range of goods and services, achieving:

- Value for money gains through economies of scale (supplier discounts on volume)
- Efficiencies through rationalisation of the supply chain
- Efficiencies through the standardisation of components
- Influence over product quality and development.

Research on procurement in the social housing sector by the CIH and NHF, (supported by the Housing Corporation) at the time of the Gershon Report, found that:

- Procurement was not widely regarded as a strategic issue
- Procurement was usually on the basis of 'supply and fit'

- Where procurement of materials and labour were split, substantial savings and other benefits were seen
- There were few effective partnership agreements with suppliers.

The conclusion was that very substantial efficiency gains could be achieved by the national procurement of materials for repairs on a consortium basis, and even greater efficiency gains through local co-operation on the procurement of labour. Following from this, CLG recognised the importance of collective procurement and appointed a National Change Agent for housing (**www.ncahousing.org.uk**) to support the creation of local consortia for capital programmes, promoting good practice and supporting the measurement and reporting of efficiency gains.

London ALMO Procurement Network (LAPN)

LAPN consists of ten ALMOs covering 150,000 dwellings. The aim is to provide partner contractors with a continuous programme of work and reasonable profit while gaining a 20% reduction in costs.

LAPN is jointly owned by all the members. The management board, steering group and delivery team look after joint procurement and improvement issues either directly or through joint improvement initiatives. Contractors are selected on two criteria. First, their experience of delivering housing projects on time and budget. Second, evidence of skills required in partnering, including product innovation, ability to work collaboratively, and with process in place to improve quality and productivity.

LAPN's Centre of Excellence is concerned with cost management and benchmarking, aiming to improve the process and change behaviour in order to deliver efficiencies. Target cost working starts with benchmarks drawn from previous similar work. The framework members are incentivised to contribute radical thinking by having their expected profit from the work protected even as they cut or eliminate their otherwise expected workload during the design workshops. The final, sign-off solution is then converted to a risk-transferred contract to be delivered, with pain/gain-sharing to help promote further cost reduction. The final outturn then becomes a new benchmark. (LAPN, 2006: *The Strategic Approach* p 5).

It is too early for a thorough evaluation of the collective procurement experience. Such evidence as there is suggests that it can achieve competitive prices on material costs for planned programmes. There is much less experience about the impact on responsive repairs, but it is seen as a missed opportunity (Audit Commission, 2006a:25), with the expectation that more will be done in the future on the joint procurement of repairs materials and cross-sector working.

It is likely that, within boundaries, economies of scale can result in better value for money, and collective procurement is one way of achieving this. But more information is needed on any diminishing returns that might show efficiencies tailing-off beyond a threshold volume. If this was the case, larger housing organisations may be able to secure these threshold volumes without acting collaboratively. This evaluation must take into account the internal costs of the procurement process. Smaller organisations are the more obvious target for joint procurement, but for those specialist organisations operating regionally or nationally, process review may demonstrate that overall delivery costs need to be addressed before looking specifically at material costs.

7.5 Supply chain management

Control over the supply chain is the thinking behind collective procurement and partnering in general. There are a variety of arrangements:

- Materials supplied to an organisation's own depot by a builders' merchant on a draw-down basis
- Operative going to a local branch of the builders' merchant to pick from a pre-supplied bin
- Delivery to site
- Imprest stock on vans.

In all cases the advantage being sought is that all purchasing and supply is handled by a specialist, providing good stock control and simplified invoicing. If this outcome is delivered, there are potential savings in operative time and back-office administrative functions.

The Wrekin Trust – Supply chain

The Wrekin Trust set out to reduce costs and improve efficiency by improving the supply chain. Previously, the Trust's in-house workforce was completing about 50,000 repairs a year at an average material price of just over £35 a job, using a wide range of material suppliers all operating paper-based systems. Following user consultation and tendering, Travis Perkins was selected in 2004 as the main supply chain partner. The agreement features:

- Leasing of a facility to Travis Perkins as the single access point for maintenance supplies
- Agreed standard product list
- Electronic transfer of job instructions and orders for materials
- Materials delivered to operatives or to the tenant's home
- Van stocks are monitored electronically

→

- Customers electronically sign the handheld screen to acknowledge completion
- Invoices are electronically reconciled
- Open book accounting through fully audited visibility of management accounts
- Profit share agreement with 'dividend' used to improve the service to tenants.

The key benefits are:
- Customer satisfaction increased from 83% to 94%, partly because the system makes it more likely that the operative will arrive with the right materials to do the job
- Ending the use of multiple suppliers, and with this, losing the inefficiencies of trades people driving from one supplier to another
- Consistency of product quality using one supplier and a standard range of products providing a better way to monitor quality and defects. The 'pick list' of materials is tailored to the Trust's requirements
- Supply chain partner acts as an adviser in the continuous review of products
- First year savings of over £300,000 on material purchase and over £100,000 on overheads. The e-business solution removed paperwork and resulted in small salary savings
- Order and invoice arrangements with electronic monitoring of van stocks reduce the opportunity for fraud
- Auditable Open Book arrangements with Profit Share. A profit share return of £13,300 was achieved in year one and similar returns have featured in each subsequent trading year. This has been used for tenants' maintenance awareness training days
- Continuous improvement mechanisms include user forums on product developments with Trust staff and tenants, manufacturers and other partners.

7.6 Partnership with other housing organisations

The business demand to deliver a better service at lower cost means that all organisations have to undertake periodic fundamental reviews of the way they deliver services, and for smaller organisations in particular the idea of partnership should be investigated.

Partnering can involve internal or external partners or be a cross-sector arrangement. The Audit Commission (2006a:5) commented on the lack of examples of where organisations had jointly procured a partnering arrangement for responsive repairs with neighbouring housing organisations. However, there are various types of partnership activity that have been explored:

- Service provision. Setting up a new call centre may be uneconomic. A larger call centre can afford to operate for longer hours and invest in more sophisticated technology. Using an established call centre owned by another housing association might be attractive.

- Regional partnering. Starting from scratch on partnering contracts for responsive and planned works may be an option. But it might be possible to expand existing arrangements put in place by other housing organisations. There may be joint benefits in terms of shared information systems and greater volumes of work.

- Contractor services. DSOs already undertake work for other housing organisations. There is an opportunity to develop this as a genuine partnership.

Contractor services

Community Building Services (CBS) is an example of a partnership approach where a DSO provides a repairs and maintenance service for a number of other housing association clients including its parent organisation – William Sutton Homes. It operates a call centre including out-of-hours emergencies, answering the phone in the name of the caller's housing organisation.

The Audit Commission (2008:49) found that smaller housing associations struggled to put the basics of procurement in place. They did not have the time or capacity to consider more sophisticated options such as partnering. These comments were made about procurement generally, not specifically repairs and maintenance, but the conclusion was '...the most effective solutions may involve the use of consortia and the sharing of a procurement specialist...While they have the potential to deliver greater efficiency, these solutions are sometimes seen as challenges to organisations' autonomy. Other associations are more positive, and believe they can access efficiency savings while maintaining distinctiveness.'

For this reason, small organisations in particular should consider becoming associated with existing local arrangements. For example, if a housing organisation already has a partnered responsive repair service the infrastructure is in place, and the real costs of extending this service are likely to be lower than starting from scratch. Working with near neighbours is a hurdle to overcome, but in the desire to offer a better service, there is the risk of spending a lot of money setting up a competing service that is no better. Professional rivalry and the desire for service differentiation should not force housing organisations into a position where they are taking risks they do not have the capacity to manage and in pursuit of uncertain results that do not have obvious benefits for their tenants.

However small or diverse the organisation might be, the need for efficiencies means looking for volume on the procurement of materials. There are various approaches, including the development of existing supplier relationships, while material procurement options include both consortia and commercial supply chain management. Small, locally based housing organisations will need to look very carefully at joining forces with others. Specialist national organisations need to look at what works best in terms of the type of service they deliver.

7.7 Partnering

Partnering is a form of collaborative working between clients, consultants, contractors and suppliers. It seeks to avoid the confrontation associated with traditional construction contracts. As such it is seen as one approach to procurement, as an integrated and co-ordinated team to achieve common objectives and shared benefits. The relationship is based on mutual objectives, an agreed method of problem resolution and an active search for continuous measurable improvements. The aim is to establish a long term relationship, with both client and contractor committing to a process of continuous improvement. The long term relationship permits the contractor to improve the supply chain and pass some of the discounts and benefit of certainty on to the client. On the quality side, the contractor has the time to develop an understanding of the client's requirements and organise themselves to provide better customer care.

- The Housing Forum has a web-based toolkit that provides guidance on partnering for the housing sector at **www.constructingexcellence.org.uk**
- The Audit Commission published an efficiency pack: *Partnering in responsive and planned maintenance*. This contains examples of organisations with experience in modern procurement practices.
- Guidance on best practice on construction procurement can be found in the OGC Achieving Excellence Guides at **www.ogc.gov.uk**

Why partnering?

The debate surrounding the Latham and Egan reports was about procuring better value through an improved relationship between client and contractor in order to increase efficiency, enhance quality and provide better customer service. At the heart of the analysis was a concern about the adversarial relationship between client and contractor. The Egan report emphasised the need to build effective partnerships to improve communication, reduce administration and share resources.

To avoid adversarial conflicts, the aim of partnering is to create a strong relationship built on mutual trust, taking the right approach with the right people, with agreed risk sharing and managing a successful outcome for both parties. The remarks of a Housing Forum publication (2000) are worth repeating:

- There is no one model of partnering
- It does not mean doing the same thing better, it means achieving a radical change in approach, organisation and process
- It is not a quick fix, and success depends on the commitment of partners and their organisations
- The nature and quality of team relationships are crucial, with effective communications and flexibility being essential.

Repairs and maintenance is a good opportunity for partnering, providing scope for developing relationships with contractors that are open, sharing risks and rewards and encouraging innovation. The aim should be to provide a streamlined and efficient service to tenants that is uncomplicated, minimises processes, reduces paper and avoids duplication of effort. The sharing of systems can help communication and reduce bureaucracy. Work with the supply chain offers the opportunity for better value through standardisation, volume and control of specification. Developing shared systems of performance monitoring can avoid the client and contractor inspecting each other.

Bristol City Council – Heating partnership

The Heating Partnership was the first long term partnering agreement implemented by Bristol City Council. It is a seven year arrangement (five years plus two, subject to performance) for work valued at around £50 million. Customers are represented on the core group and have been involved in developing the partnership structure and monitoring performance. Other members of the partnership are the contractor manufacturers and suppliers. The partnership is based on:

- An agreed annual fixed breakdown and failure charge for system maintenance that is reviewed annually and was reduced by 20% on the first review
- Failed boilers issued on a three day notice but next day replacement usually achieved
- Agreed profits and open book cost management
- Bulk invoicing
- Co-location of staff.

→

The outcomes are:

- Reduced staff costs – agreed specifications avoid pre-inspection, co-location and bulk invoicing
- Economies of scale – guaranteed work flow allows planning, avoids waste and allows consolidation of overheads
- Supply chain – including the supplier in the partnership ensures that material cost savings are realised by the partnership
- Strict quality checks have led to a an extended five year warranty on all boilers
- Site delivery of heating packs reduces time wasted collecting components
- 98% recycling of waste materials.

While effective partnering can contribute to successful outcomes and deliver significant improvements in value for money, it requires effort and commitment from both sides. The partnering agreement should include:

- Incentives for all parties
- A shared risk register
- A joint project board with defined roles for all involved
- An agreed performance management system and criteria
- Agreement on the means of communication
- A process of sharing knowledge and experience.

It could also feature open book accounting for both parties, adding transparency in the area of actual costs and agreed profit margins. This might include:

- An agreed schedule of rates or target costs
- Turnaround times for responsive repairs and completion timescales for planned programmes
- Economies through bulk purchasing efficiencies
- Open book disclosure of all costs and time incurred
- Regular reviews of working procedures and performance indicators
- Annual strategic reviews
- Improvement reviews that produce mutually acceptable quality enhancements
- Analysis of work performed against types of property
- Feedback from customers
- Supplier review by all parties including tenants
- Continuous improvement reviews.

'Open book' is a term that is widely associated with partnering. It has two limitations. First, it needs to operate in an environment where the client already has reliable information on costs, quality and demand. This cost profile information should ideally be available before moving into a partnering arrangement.

Second, open book means nothing until it is defined. The questions are, how open and which book? The Audit Commission commented:

> *'Open book accounting was identified by organisations as a mechanism to assist in the identification of costs. However, the majority of organisations contacted who cited open book accounting were not able to expand how they used it other than for cost identification purposes. Open book accounting is being underused as a tool for identifying and reducing risk.'* (Audit Commission, 2006a:22).

Sheffield City Council and Kier – Joint venture

Sheffield LLP is a joint venture vehicle with Sheffield City Council as a minority shareholder. This partnership was awarded a repairs and maintenance contract in 2003 (under PPC2000) that coverd all Council homes and buildings (libraries, schools etc) and runs for ten years, with an option of review after seven years. It involved the transfer of the City's DLO to the new company.

The objectives included:

- The introduction of a comprehensive performance management framework that measures service performance and improvement
- The consolidation of existing depots into one main depot
- The operation of a service centre to take repair requests
- Investing in training, in information systems, and in management capacity.

Positive outcomes included:

- The call centre improved customer access to repair ordering (and freed up existing housing staff for other priorities). The call centre staff were supported by technical staff, which helped to improve the efficiency of the service
- New working practices on service delivery speeded up work and improved response times, These included mobile communications, dedicated functional teams, stocked vans.
- Moving from several depots to one released land valued at over £4 million
- Effective customer participation in all aspects of service planning and delivery to provide a customer focused service
- Improved management and performance reporting
- A reduction in schedule of rates from day one

→

- Guaranteed annual payment equivalent to the old DLO profit
- The LLP partnership structure allowed for significant financial and tax advantages for the Council in relation to future profits
- No costs associated with re-tendering exercises.

Fuller details can be found in a Project Information Brief on the Public Private Partnership website **www.4ps.gov.uk**

Objectives

The objectives of partnering must be clearly defined. The opportunity for cost savings may be an ill-judged assumption, particularly if more responsibility for contract delivery is being passed on to the contractor. The costs may be equivalent when taking into account any internal savings, and the question is about measurable improvements in quality. An assessment must therefore look both at cost and quality, and this should be reflected in the objectives.

Example partnering objectives

Provide a service that represents value for money

- Customers to experience a real improvement in service quality
- Active involvement in community sustainability strategies, particularly local job and training opportunities
- Pricing systems to be replaced by approaches to costing that are open and provide value for money.

Improve areas of key performance

- Develop working relationships with contractors that will last and lead to service improvements that can be measured and monitored
- Involve customers in the process of determining and monitoring service standards
- Deliver a positive change in culture through the development of trust, openness and respect
- Establish a positive and proactive process for resolving problems and disputes.

Increase efficiency in the service delivery process

- Include supply chain partners in all aspects of the partnering process
- Exclude unnecessary processes, minimise bureaucracy and utilise resources efficiently.

→

Minimise financial and other risks

- Develop a culture of risk sharing and open accountability
- Evaluate the partnership's exposure to risk and prepare an exit strategy if things go wrong
- Minimise but do not ignore the need for dispute resolution and termination.

The partners should be clear about who is responsible for aspects of service delivery. It should be agreed how complaints are handled, and this should be communicated to tenants. All parties have to be committed to learning from complaints.

Selecting a partner

The right partner is the key to delivery. Partnering and team work depend on relationships. This said, selecting a partner starts with identifying a combination of technical ability and compatibility. The partner should:

- Understand partnering
- Demonstrate their commitment and be sympathetic to the culture and goals of the partnership
- Be committed to quality and have working quality and information management systems
- Demonstrate a flexible approach and show a willingness to learn, to be innovative, and to take the longer view.

The selection process will involve reference site visits including discussion with residents and clients. It is very important to know who will manage the service and what this management will involve.

Knightstone Housing Association – Selecting partners

Knightstone modernised its approach to procuring responsive maintenance services, having encouraged feedback from residents, staff and contractors. Problems included:

- Up to 16 different contractors working to annually-let schedule of rates contracts
- An adversarial and unwieldy contract
- Lack of long-term certainty for contractors
- Cumbersome administration, with around 38,000 individual invoices processed annually.

Knightstone embarked on a six month recruitment programme to select a number of new partners to deliver and develop the service over the next five years. Key aspects of the selection process included:

→

- Intensive tenant involvement throughout the process – in establishing new service standards, checking the prospective contractors for quality, formal interviews and speaking to contractors' referees
- Setting up a staff/tenant 'check team' which spent a day with each of the shortlisted contractors, watching, listening and scoring them against pre-determined selection criteria
- 'Van checks' – a member of staff spent a day with an operative from each contractor, the results influencing the final decision-making process
- A contractors' day organised for those shortlisted, to explain the selection process and criteria and to use the session as a starting point for getting to know new partners.

The resulting repairs service features:
- A reduced number of contractors – from 16 to 6
- A new 5 year term partnering contract
- New performance measures based around what matters to customers:
  - end-to-end completion times (7.8 days on average)
  - appointments made within 2 hours of receiving the order (currently achieving 96% appointments made and kept)
  - customer satisfaction checked by phone call on all completed orders (95% satisfaction with the overall service and the repair itself)
  - tenant volunteers participating in monthly contractor review meetings
  - all performance information is shared with the contractors openly; they can each see how the others are performing and league tables are discussed together at quarterly partnering meetings
- Paperless administration – data on completions, claims for payment, certificates and invoices are processed automatically
- Innovation and efficiency measures agreed at the start of each year with each contractor. Practical initiatives include announced 'contractor days' on larger estates – tenants can either book work in on the days or call in the contractors when they see them.

A DSO is a legitimate candidate for partnering. DSOs were not very common in the RSL sector, but this has changed as a result of LSVT. A well run DSO should be able to compete against a private contractor, with the added advantage of VAT savings for housing organisations. The best are also able to commit themselves to training and employment initiatives that support the organisation's business objectives. The regulators expect organisations to be able to demonstrate the competitiveness of internal service provision when compared with external providers.

Guidance on DSO assessment can be found in the Housing Corporation's Good Practice Guide for DLOs (2002)

Measurement

Change is not an easy process, and the move towards partnering has had its fair share of blind adherence, enthusiastic early adopters and cynical detractors. Partnering is not just a badge, and it does not mean that all the parties have totally shared objectives. The opportunities that can stem from partnering come with the responsibility to be a better client, a better contractor and a better team. And at the heart of this is the measurement of performance.

The key messages on performance measurement are:

- Use the minimum number of indicators necessary to establish that partners are fulfilling their obligations
- Focus on key service objectives rather than what can easily be measured
- Evaluate against outcomes that can be compared with other providers
- Put as much information as possible into the public domain.

The methods of performance evaluation include:

- User surveys to give a periodic view of service performance (with user panels offering some longitudinal comparison)
- Process monitoring, which can provide a trend analysis
- Output monitoring against service deliverables, measured over time
- Outcome monitoring against service objectives to support continuous improvement.

Partnering is a process, and measurement is important to its successful delivery. Organisations are not always able to quantify the benefits or gains of partnering because the outcomes are not evaluated. The Audit Commission commented:

> *'...the work being done by individual housing organisations to identify costs is not routinely being brought together with the benefits data to give an overall judgement on whether partnering is working for them and that the benefits outweigh the costs and the improvements are as a consequence of the partnering arrangement.'* (Audit Commission, 2006a:60).

Kier Sheffield LLP – Partnership performance management

Kier Sheffield LLP recognises the value of good performance management and monitoring. Service monitoring is done through a web-based Panagraph Performance Management System (Panagraph Management Systems Ltd). This is an interactive performance management tool which displays performance in a readily analysed graphical format. It monitors key areas of the partnership and thereby supports the continuous improvement process. It allows:

→

- Several measures of performance to be viewed simultaneously
- A single source of data, ensuring the same information is being provided by all parties
- Actual performance against targets to be shown
- Trends over time and by sub-sets of the data to be shown
- Access to the underlying data through drill down.

The approach is unique in a number of ways:

- The use of graphics to monitor performance. It is a development of thinking that has been around as long as Executive Information Systems, but it is still relatively rare
- Acknowledged dependence on good data (and a backup of detailed data definitions) and a well managed monthly process of data submission, checking and review, followed by action plans to address performance issues. The performance indicators (known in Sheffield as SKIs – Sheffield Kier Indicators) are defined, with the method of measurement, how the data is collected and the method of validation to ensure they continue to provide valid and accurate performance data
- The model can be accessed by tenants because it is internet based. It provides everyone with direct access to performance data about responsive repairs. It is interactive, so it is possible to analyse information, identify key issues and make plans to deal with any poor performance. Joint action plans are created with customers, the client and Kier to remedy any issues arising. This approach in Sheffield assisted the partnership in achieving Beacon Status in 2005.

View the live model at **www.sheffieldhomes.org.uk/performance-at-your-fingertips**

The choice of method is not the most significant factor in successful procurement. The Audit Commission made a comparison between the performance of housing associations on three repairs performance targets with the method of delivery of the contract. There was no clear correlation between performance and delivery method, and no clear correlation between efficiency savings and method of delivery. From these findings their conclusion was that the choice of procurement method is only one factor in determining the extent of savings. Other equally important factors include:

- Clarity of leadership
- The appointment of a senior procurement champion
- Skills
- Active contract and performance management
- Supply chain management (Audit Commission, 2008).

Summary

- Housing organisations should have an approved procurement strategy.

- The client's role in managing the contract is to be clear about what the objectives are, how these are to be delivered and the measurements that need to be in place to make sure this happens.

- Look at the way services are to be delivered and the skills available to function as an effective client.

- Decide whether greater contractor involvement fits the organisation's business plan, or whether in-house delivery provides a better fit with customer service objectives.

- Consider whether the best is being made of contractor skills under current arrangements.

- Collaborative working and collective procurement are aspects of partnership working driven by an awareness that good and efficient service are partly influenced by scale. While an organisation will wish to deliver a service that tenants want and can influence, this also has to be a service that the organisation can afford, and the search for efficiencies must take advantage of scale in terms of infrastructure, procedures, procurement and management expertise.

- Review the position on collective procurement and be able to justify why the organisation is not working with others to gain the benefits of scale.

- Look at whether there are services or functions that could be done by or in partnership with other housing organisations.

- Check progress on partnering. Question what the organisation might want to get out of it. How would a relationship be set up, managed and developed? Can existing relationships be improved? What can the market offer?

- If partnering is in place, is it being done well? Could it be done better? Are there gains that could be made in specific areas if not across the whole function?

- It is important that assumed efficiency gains can be quantified. The Audit Commission (2006a:9) has made the point that, while partnering in responsive and planned repairs has the potential to deliver efficiency gains, these have not always been quantified, and that the benefits have not been routinely evaluated.

CHAPTER 8

MEASURING SERVICE PERFORMANCE

Service improvement means doing things better. It is about having processes that work, low overheads, works that provide good value for money and a service that provides tenants with what they want. The measures that matter are whether tenants are satisfied, whether the service meets performance standards and whether the organisation can afford to deliver the service. In these terms, this chapter looks at how to evaluate tenants' views about the service and assess service quality in terms of costs and quality.

8.1 Service promise

The asset management strategy should be supported by a comprehensive repairs and maintenance policy and service plans which show what will be delivered, when and how this will be done. They should also include the standards to be applied to the measurement of performance. Typical coverage is shown in the box below.

Suggested headings for a repair and maintenance policy

Aims and objectives

Service standards

Reporting on service standards

Landlord responsibilities

Tenant responsibilities

Recharging

Redecoration

Tenant improvements

Right to repair

Aids and adaptations

→

Responsive	Fault reporting
	Appointments
	Works ordering
	Responsive targets
	Inspections
Planned	Preventative and cyclical works
	Gas safety checks
	Renewals
	Improvements
	Priorities
	Consultation
	Notification
	Contract delivery and management
Voids	Management
	Standards
Contractor payment	
Insurance reclaims	
Approved contractors	
Tendering procedure	
Performance measurement	
Complaints procedure	

Service standards must be agreed, but they can be tailored to meet local needs and refined to reflect the different requirements of different client groups. The aim, particularly for larger organisations, is to deliver service variation at no additional cost. The easiest way to reduce costs is to simplify and centralise. This takes out cost duplication and inefficiency. But it can also be unresponsive and lacking in local autonomy. The challenge is to provide a strong, simple and effective framework while permitting a significant amount of local empowerment. This allows local staff to do the job in the way they see best, while tenants feel they matter and receive a service attuned to local needs.

8.2 Involving customers

The key to a good repairs and maintenance service is tenant satisfaction and affordability, and the measurement of service performance reflects these ambitions. As considered in Chapter 3, the repairs service is a key interaction between the housing organisation and the tenant, and there are measures of satisfaction to be collected at the point of service delivery. This feedback must be collected regularly and be an integral part of the process. Equally importantly it must be used. The data has to be collected, analysed and then applied in a way that demonstrates users are having an influence on service delivery.

Tenants are at the centre of quality measurement, and should be involved in a variety of ways. Qualitative measurement should aim at precision, consistency and benchmarking. Data must be collected as part of the process, be made widely available to tenants, and subject to much more detailed analysis to understand patterns of failure, demand and customer requirements.

8.3 Measuring service quality

Collecting performance data

Organisations collect a great deal of data as part of their work. Before collecting more it is worth asking whether the best possible use is being made of what already exists.

Using existing information: checklist

- Consider what information is collected on a routine basis that might contribute to a better understanding of service quality issues

- Consider whether small changes to the way that administrative and management data is collected could make it more useful for the assessment of service quality

- Appraise the limitations of existing information to develop an understanding of where the gaps in knowledge are

- Undertake a review of routine data collection to assess how far it serves quality assessment and continuous improvement

- Be prepared to change what is measured to reflect changing circumstances and priorities. Involve staff and service users in a review and in defining any new measures

- Use existing information in a more deliberately consultative and proactive way

- When collecting new data make sure you know in advance how all new data is to be used and by whom, that is, 'design use in'.

(Communities Scotland, 2006:62)

Data about responsive performance should be collected as part of the process, not as an add-on requirement. A typical list is set out overleaf.

Quantitative measures: Responsive repairs

- Numbers or faults and repairs by category of work, with ability to undertake more sophisticated analysis.
- Breakdown of emergency, urgent and routine.
- Accuracy of works ordered against work competed.
- Completion within target time.
- Performance of the appointment system.
- Number of jobs completed on first visit by emergency, urgent and routine
- Call-backs to correct work already completed.

In defining measures of performance, housing organisations need to be aware of regulatory requirements, but should also consult with tenants about service expectations and work with benchmark clubs to agree common definitions. Measures to be considered include the following:

- **Overall time from fault report to works completed.** The start point is when the tenant reports a fault, not when the order is raised. The finish point is when all the work associated with the fault report is competed. A fault may require a number of repairs, but it is the overall elapsed time that matters if the tenant feels there has been delay.

- **Accuracy of the fault report.** When the contractor attends and finds a repair unrelated to the recorded fault, some systems cancel and raise a new order. This is confusing. It is clearer to change the repair but hold a history, ensuring that the cost of the original fault is held to compare with the actual repair carried out. Substantial or systematic variation would require investigation. The aim should be to track any pattern of misreporting of faults. Some may have trivial implications. But if some cost money they are a priority for more detailed scrutiny.

- **Appointments kept.** It is common for contractors to record an appointment as kept when they arrive on time and fail to gain access. This results in data that conflicts with tenants' accounts of the appointment system. It is better to record the appointment as unsuccessful with a coded reason. In this way everyone can work towards a more effective appointment system instead of labouring under the illusion that all is working well.

- **Number of appointments.** For similar reasons housing organisations should record the number of repairs carried out by appointment, the percentage made and the percentage kept. There is little value in the statistic that 85% of appointments were kept if this obscures the fact that only 20% of repairs were done by appointment.

- **Work completed at first visit.** Some housing organisations use this measure but exclude emergency or out of hours work. This is not recommended. Emergency work is to make safe, and at this point is a completed job. Any follow-up should be raised as a new repair, albeit one associated with the original fault.

Tollcross Housing Association – Accurate reporting

Tollcross Housing Association has developed a system to accurately monitor and report responsive repairs. Association staff are in contact with contractors by telephone throughout each working day to find out when jobs were completed. The call centre which provides the Association's out of hours service reports each morning by fax and telephone on the emergencies received overnight, with the time each repair was reported, the contractor's time of attendance and the time the emergency was resolved. The Association requires contractors to manually log the time they uplift works orders and record the date when work was completed. The Association then validates its performance by cross-referring the information in the contractor's log with its maintenance recording system.

Ways of getting things right are not always innovative and cutting-edge. This is an example of how a small association takes care to ensure that it achieves accurate reporting of response times against targets. Attention to detail is a lesson that can be applied by others irrespective of size and electronic sophistication.

HouseMark (2008a) has recently produced guidance for tenants and landlords on how to develop and monitor local performance measures. The guidance was based on the findings from a range of tenant and landlord focus groups which were held across England in 2007.

The primary aim of the project was to provide guidance that will help housing organisations to develop, with their tenants, customer-focused performance measures associated with core landlord services, against which standards can be set and performance monitored.

Though not intended to be prescriptive, the following are a set of suggested customer focused performance indicators and measures for responsive repairs:

Suggested PIs	Comments
COST MEASURES Major and cyclical (planned repairs) as a percentage of all repairs spend.	This is a useful value for money (VFM) measure as it is generally held that the overall repairs spend should be weighted to planned works.
Responsive repairs cost per property (client-side costs).	By collecting client-side costs only (ie the cost to the housing organisation of organising the repair as opposed to doing the repair work), the costs associated with administration of the repairs service can be isolated and housing organisations can then determine whether there is a high spend on administration. →

Suggested PIs	Comments
COST MEASURES – continued Basket of common repairs.	This is essentially a list of typical repairs and associated costs.
(HARD) PERFORMANCE MEASURES Number of responsive repairs orders per property. Number of recharges made to tenants and percentage recovered. Percentage of response repairs where an appointment was made and kept. Percentage of response repairs where an appointment was cancelled by: • the contractor • the tenant Percentage aborted calls (no access). Percentage repairs done right first time.	These measures can be even more useful if supported by contextual information that outlines the type of repair work occurring and if problems are associated with a specific area of work.
(SOFT) SATISFACTION MEASURES Generally, how satisfied or dissatisfied are you with the ways your housing association deals with repairs and maintenance? Thinking about your last completed repair, how would you rate it in terms of: a) being told when workers would call b) time taken before work started c) speed with which work was completed d) attitude of workers e) overall quality of repair work f) keeping dirt and mess to a minimum? Percentage tenants satisfied with the system for reporting repairs In terms of the appointment: • % tenants satisfied with the appointment system, possibly further broken down by: • were you happy with the choice of times? • did operatives attend when agreed?	This measure breaks down the customer experience of the repairs service into its component parts. It is useful to be able to pinpoint where things are going wrong and take action. It may be more realistic to collect this information from a representative sample of tenants.

Interestingly, there are no suggested indicators associated with routine repair timescales. The research found that this was not something that tenants viewed as a priority. Over-emphasis on speed of completion could actually detract from customer focus and what really matters to tenants. Timescale performance measures can be useful in understanding and reviewing the actual process. However, the consistent message is that tenants value the following: certainty (turn up and do what was agreed at the agreed time); convenience (choice over time slot, job done in one visit where possible and with no mess); and quality (no reworking).

Planned and cyclical programmes

Compared with responsive repairs, performance data for planned and cyclical programmes has attracted less attention. It is perhaps the case that responsive repairs have always been seen as a service, while planned programmes have tended to be driven by contract procedures. More consultation about standards and priorities will help, but there needs to be a more customer-focused element to performance data. It is here that systems are generally unhelpful. Only with integrated project management software will housing organisations be able to track and report on progress. This requires projects to report at unit level, which is essential if costs are to be properly attributed. However, there will be an overhead if contractors are required to monitor start and finish dates against individual units. It is even more difficult to record events such as tenant communications and contacts, but obviously it is important to record the reasons why a property was excluded from any programme of works, for example because of tenant refusal.

From an organisational perspective the important facts about a planned programme are that it is:

- On plan and on budget
- The relevant works are properly recorded against the relevant properties.

The missing element is what the tenants think about the process and whether they are happy with the end result. Here good housing organisations might consider undertaking specific attitude surveys on completion of the works programme. The survey design will be determined by programme delivery and scale. For example, a rolling programme of component replacement might be treated differently to a whole house estate modernisation scheme. This does not preclude a standard set of approaches or a proper analysis of the results. Only in this way will the organisation learn about the shortcomings of the process, the quality of the work and the performance of the contractor.

Guidance for tenants and landlords on performance measures for major works are set out in the following table (HouseMark, 2008a).

Suggested PIs	Comments
COST MEASURES Major and cyclical cost per property. Major and cyclical client costs as % overall repairs spend.	As with 'responsive repairs cost per property (client-side costs)' in the responsive repairs section, this PI seeks to isolate the comparative cost of administration.
(HARD) PERFORMANCE MEASURES Percentage of social housing rental stock failing to meet the relevant housing quality standard. Average SAP rating (energy efficiency) of social housing rental dwellings.	
(SOFT) SATISFACTION MEASURES Percentage of tenants satisfied with the quality of their newly-built homes. Capital works – resident satisfaction – product, ie scope and quality of the work done. Capital works – resident satisfaction – overall service.	

In terms of cyclical programmes, gas servicing is usually subject to fairly rigorous reporting and independent audit as part of compliance. This needs information system support, and only the smallest organisations can consider operating this process using spreadsheets. It is a business critical system that needs to be robust, properly backed-up and sharing information with other corporate systems and users.

The essential characteristics of gas servicing are shared by other mechanical and electrical (M&E) servicing contracts. It is likely that the complexity of service charge management will force housing organisations to pay more attention to this area in the near future; therefore it makes sense to anticipate the requirement and start now. Implement or extend gas servicing systems to cover the recording and servicing of all M&E installations. Begin by reporting on the performance of service contracts against the schedule, and then analyse the data to see whether there is scope for efficiencies through the combination of service contracts or the standardisation of equipment.

Collecting cost data

Cyclical maintenance

All servicing and cyclical costs (including client-side costs) need to be attributed to individual units in order to facilitate the calculation of service charges. With this comes the ability to analyse the data by type of work, area and other variables, and this is the starting point when identifying efficiency savings. It is an area of costs that has been overlooked, partly because it is the addition of a number of relatively low value items. However, cyclical maintenance and servicing can cost in the range £150-£250 per property every year, which could easily exceed the whole of one month's rent income. Across the stock as a whole, year after year, it is an area where small percentage savings can add up to a significant reduction in budget costs.

Planned maintenance

The costs of planned programmes also need to be linked back to individual properties. Only in this way can housing organisations obtain a complete picture of how the stock performs in terms of a return. A particular problem with planned programmes, however, is the consistent treatment of overheads. The ambition is to attribute to a unit the cost of doing the work. The cost should include materials and labour inclusive of fees, VAT and preliminaries. It should take a consistent approach to management preliminaries (client-side costs) such as the apportionment of tenant liaison costs.

Responsive repairs

Rather similar problems occur when looking at the costs of the responsive repairs service. This falls into two parts. The first is the coding of works to responsive that really belong elsewhere – planned works done on a responsive basis. The second is the allocation of management costs. Some organisations carry all the client-side costs themselves. In others, the contractor provides a full service and the client role is limited to scrutiny and audit. One approach, suggested by HQN (2007), is to apply cost modifiers along the following lines:

- Plus 7% for an inclusive contractor service
- Plus 12% for mixed responsibilities
- Plus 20% where the client takes fault reports, does pre and post inspections and monitors tenant satisfaction.

The importance of getting costs right depends on purpose. Definitions need to be very clear when making benchmark comparisons. When looking at in-house trends the aim is to reveal the important variables. For example, if responsive costs do not reflect call centre overheads it will mask the impact of tenants' chasing calls. If the volume of calls is not monitored and costed there may be no incentive to reduce the number of times a tenant calls to check on progress. An inefficient service looks more efficient if some of the costs are disguised in a different budget.

Organisations should analyse cost data for responsive repairs very thoroughly. Look at what work gets done to what property, and at the characteristics of tenants most likely to be reporting repairs. A small number of tenants report a disproportionate number of repairs. If they reported an average number, overall costs would fall.

8.4 Continuous improvement

Service improvement is the objective: either doing things better, or getting the same result for less cost or effort. Data analysis and monitoring is part of the process of continuous improvement. If trend reports are adverse, there is a clear problem requiring a response. If trends are flat or improving there remains the question of benchmarks. How well does the service compare with others? These comparisons must be made on a realistic basis and should be used as a way of learning how to improve performance.

Housing organisations should have in place their own set of internal processes for continuous improvement, and there is nothing special about their application to repairs and maintenance.

Best value

- Use of Best Value techniques – see CLG local government performance site – **www.bvpi.gov.uk**; in Scotland, **www.scotland.gov.uk/topics**
- NHF (2004:8-10)
- Best Value used in Wales (see NAW, 2001; WAG, 2006)

Benchmarking should be used to demonstrate quality and value for money. It is not an end in itself. It should lead to real improvements by identifying and learning from the practices of good performers. It should also be used to give tenants sources of comparison against which they can judge the quality of the service they use.

There are a number of benchmarking clubs operating in social housing, but an organisation's own improvement over time is at least as relevant as its performance relative to other housing organisations. This is the reason time series data is important, for example HouseMark's Capital Works Benchmarking System. Benchmarking results can be compared by type of work, by time period, and against other users and the Constructing Excellence national data set (see NCA 2007 for further discussion).

This need to compare means that housing organisations should be completely open about their performance. All the data should be available in the public domain as part of a wider corporate strategy to inform customers. This is about openness and accountability. The Cave review highlighted the importance of increasing expectations of accountability to service users. An emerging theme of regulation is that it should promote choice for tenants, empowered by access to information about the relative performance of their housing organisation. The best organisations will find it benefits them as well as their tenants.

Summary

- The service promise should be clearly defined so that performance criteria are explicit.
- Tenants should be involved in setting and measuring service standards.
- Use a variety of methods for measuring customer satisfaction.
- Analyse the data to understand underlying trends.
- Collect performance data as part of the process and focus on the proper measurement of what is important.
- Collect cost data so that works can be attributed back to individual units.
- Analyse this data to see the underlying patterns of service use.
- Aim for continuous improvement through techniques like best value review and benchmarking.
- Be completely open about performance.

CHAPTER 9

SERVICE REVIEW AND DEVELOPMENT

There are many factors influencing the current and future shape of the repairs and maintenance service; the changing policy context; cost pressures on investment plans; the additional complexity of mixed tenures; the need to deliver improved levels of service at lower cost. To achieve this, housing organisations must be able to continuously review the current services they provide to assess how they are shaped to meet these challenges. This chapter looks at the importance of service review, how they should be carried out and their terms of reference. There are various established methodologies that can be used. They provide a framework to ensure processes are systematically reviewed.

9.1 Service review

It is important for housing organisations to periodically undertake a fundamental assessment of the way the repairs and maintenance service is currently delivered, supported by an understanding of what tenants want and expect from the service, both now and in the future.

Service reviews should be carried out within the context of the wider asset management strategy, setting out the requirements for success and the broad terms of reference. This gives the review executive level responsibility. Recommendations arising out of the review should come back to the executive with evidence that the agreed requirements can be achieved, and this should then be delivered through a revision of service policy. This policy should consider the elements of a service together, not as separate components. Tenants do not make a distinction between responsive, cyclical and planned, so a service focused on customer requirements should not start with these divisions. The asset management strategy and the associated policies should be very clear about service goals, the principles to be applied to service design and the relative importance to be attached to outcome measures.

9.2 Consultation

There is both a regulatory requirement and a business imperative to consult with tenants about service priorities, standards and performance. Housing organisations must be able to demonstrate how their tenants influence the order in which service reviews are carried out. It is also important to engage with tenants as part of any review, using their input when looking at problem definition, service specification, service improvement, evaluation and monitoring.

There are many approaches to consultation, and most organisations would be likely to use a mix of techniques. While formal consultation with existing tenant organisations and informal groups takes place, it is important to recognise that many tenants may not wish to be part of formal groups. A variety of consultation methods and frameworks need to be established to capture the views of individual service users, from a range of sources. (Communities Scotland, 2005:2).

The mix of tools being used for consultation should not value hard data over soft; a balance should be established between qualitative and quantitative methods, such as questionnaire surveys, focus groups and information flowing back from the complaints procedure (see Chapter 3).

9.3 Equality and diversity

When completing any review of services it is essential to pay attention to identifying the needs of all sections of the customer base. Repairs and maintenance policies and services should be designed in accordance with these needs.

The key requirements in relation to repairs and maintenance services are set out in Audit Commission KLOE: Prospects for improvement (2005). They expect an organisation to:

- Have a clear understanding of its local community using all relevant information, including the input of local partners, and know its own service user profile, making necessary adjustments where this is out of step in meeting the needs of those that require services.
- Know, record, analyse and monitor information about the ethnicity, vulnerability and disability of service users and use it to ensure services are delivered appropriately and to prioritise resources.
- Provide information about services and service standards in a comprehensive range of languages and formats appropriate to service users' needs eg, large print, Braille, other languages etc.
- Work with its component communities to ensure fair representation and service take-up.

- Not discriminate against any person or other organisation on the grounds of race, ethnic origin, disability, nationality, gender, sexuality, age, class, appearance, religion, responsibility for dependants, unrelated criminal activities, being HIV positive or with AIDS, or any other matter which causes a person to be treated with injustice.

9.4 Leading the review

The job of the senior management team is to provide leadership, vision and a clear set of prioritised objectives for any service review. They should also give:

- Commitment and backing
- Adequate resources
- Clear rules
- An overall framework.

Commitment and backing

Proposals for changing and improving the repairs and maintenance service will be worked out in some detail by a team of people within the organisation. This takes time, and the resulting proposals demand the backing of the whole senior management team. The responsible director must lead or be closely involved in process review.

Resources

It is often the case that the agreed timetable for review and implementation is sensible in its own terms, but fails to reflect the demands of team members' existing jobs. The process will be more efficient, and almost certainly quicker, if review and subsequent implementation is properly resourced.

The rules

The senior management team is responsible for establishing a climate where improvement and change can take place. This means:

- Being open to criticism
- Allowing accepted wisdoms to be challenged
- Giving people the freedom to fail
- Protecting those who may be designing themselves out of a job.

The framework

It is important to be very clear about corporate objectives. Setting the strategic framework gives a business focus, making explicit the benefits that the housing organisation as client is seeking when procuring a product or service. The role of the

Executive and the Board is to define what is required and to align this with the culture and values of the organisation.

There is a key role for leadership at this level, not least because hard decisions may be required. If there is evidence that the existing stock needs more investment, how precisely is this to happen? What actions have to be taken to secure alternative sources of grant funding, borrowing or sales income? What is being done in terms of option appraisal? Has any serious work been done on stock rationalisation? (CIH, 2007a; Housing Corporation, 2007). If the problem is to be addressed within the current restricted budgets, will delayed investment or lower standards be sanctioned? If the solution is thought to be through efficiencies, precisely what grounds are there for the assumption that they can be delivered?

9.5 Terms of reference

The terms of reference of a service review need to be set with care, and should not be drawn too tightly in the early stages. Rather than looking at responsive repairs, consider looking first at the property life cycle – from development through to disposal. The repairs and maintenance service is a combination of different actions under the conventional descriptions of responsive, cyclical and planned maintenance. They are related, and a service review should start by challenging all conventional assumptions.

Delivering excellence

The criteria set by the Audit Commission when looking at prospects for improvement can provide a starting point for service review. An excellent housing organisation should have:

- A clear vision for the service which sets out what the organisation wants to achieve over the long term. It has translated its vision into tangible ambitions, aims and objectives for the future of the service. These make clear what the organisation wants to achieve to improve the overall service quality for users both now and in the future.

- Aims that are stretching and which aspire to make a real and measurable difference for service users, particularly the most vulnerable. They make clear the longer-term (next 5-10 years) sustainable outcomes that can realistically be achieved. There is a clear indication of the challenging outcomes and targets that it is seeking to achieve and the timescales it is working to.

- Developed its aims based on a sound knowledge of the challenges and opportunities faced within the service including the views and needs of users now and in the future.

Audit Commission KLOE: Prospects for improvement (2005)

When looking at the way the service is provided the review should ask fundamental questions:

- How does the repairs and maintenance service support the asset management strategy?

- How good is the service? Does it meet the business criteria? Do the individual elements perform well? Does it understand that customer needs are not uniform, and that the service has to meet different requirements?

- What is the true cost of providing the service? What proportion of the rent does it consume? Do tenants think the repair component of their rent is well spent?

- How is the service to be provided so that the work gets done to a high standard within target timescales and generally on the first visit?

- Is it possible to reduce demand for responsive repairs by meeting needs in another way?

- What is the true cost of works required to re-let a void property? Does the organisation regard a void as an opportunity for maintenance work? Or is the priority to re-let the property, doing only the minimum necessary to achieve this?

- How do void works relate to planned programmes? Are there common standards? And what opportunities are there to share procurement?

- When was the last review of the purpose and intent of the cyclical, preventative and service maintenance contracts? Is there clarity about the full scope of work being done? Is cyclical work being done in an intelligent way to delay the need for more major works?

- Is the organisation expecting to see a growth in service charge management through mixed tenure development? Have the implications been considered of the way the service may need to be restructured to take care of the new demands?

For a more comprehensive set of questions, a useful resource is the Repair and Improvement Toolkit prepared by Welsh Local Government Association (WLGA, 2007) which can be found at **www.wlga.gov.uk/housingtoolkits**

City of Edinburgh – Repair service review

The City of Edinburgh's in-house repairs provider, Edinburgh Building Services has transformed its performance in relation to the repairs and maintenance service. In 2003 the City faced a series of challenges with finances, performance and customer experience. Sickness was over 10% and staff turnover peaked at 30% a year. One in four jobs was rated as unsatisfactory by tenants, and there were 1,000 complaints a month.

→

By 2007/8, profitability and performance had significantly improved, with a 90% reduction in complaints and a 33% increase in operative productivity. Overtime had been reduced by 75% and staff satisfaction had increased from 25% to 78%. Further, waiting times for repairs reduced from 8 weeks to 6-7 working days.

The change process focused on improving staff performance and morale. The principles of change included:

- High levels of employee participation
- Encouraging innovation
- Rewarding employees who offered new ideas
- Staff rewards scheme
- Celebrating the small successes not just the formal awards.

The transformation rested on an entirely fresh approach:

- Leadership – behaviour that emphasised inclusive decision-making, strong communication, a focus on performance and a management structure with the skills, scope and ability to manage
- Priorities – the initial plan being to improve performance, stabilise the financial position, build trust and streamline key business processes
- Learning – from customers, from staff, and from other organisations, and applying this learning through changes in the way jobs were ordered, the use of technology, a new imprest stock system, a new productivity-based bonus payment giving operatives more control over the organisation of their work schedule and a work scheduling software – Opti-Time
- Managing change – setting out the key principles governing the way the organisation worked, making an impact through a series of small but significant policy or process changes, and making sure these changes were properly communicated to everyone
- Performance framework – a common framework for key performance standards across each business unit, linked to more strategic housing goals, setting improved standards and issuing guidance on how to achieve the standard
- Helping people to perform – creating a supportive environment where performance is valued and rewarded, giving clarity on priorities, communicating the importance of good performance, rewarding it through the bonus system, supporting it through training and tackling under-performance by acting early and consistently on poor performance, absence and disciplinary issues. Methods included 'aiming for excellence' workshops, team talks, job shadowing and lunchtime academies to discuss hot topics.

9.6 Methodologies

To deliver service review there are good reasons for adopting a methodology like Business Process Review (BPR) or Systems Thinking. They provide a framework to ensure that processes are reviewed systematically and analytically. However, they do not provide anything like the whole answer. No process can guarantee a successful outcome on its own. In the end, success is about people. Has the organisation got the competencies to deliver change? There is more likely to be a good result if the right people are involved in the right project at the right time. It is not just about understanding the problem and seeing a solution. It is about managing all the people who have an interest. Resistance of any kind will present barriers to change, and can slow down the process. Effective change management involves careful analysis of the current situation, securing support; tackling resistance; building commitment; remaining flexible and adjusting when problems emerge.

Service review methodologies

- Evaluative models like PEST (Political, economic, socio-cultural and technological environment, see for example Kotler, 1998) and SWOT (strengths, weaknesses, opportunities, threats) can help to describe the external influences affecting change

- Methodologies such as BPR (Hammer and Champy, 1993), System Thinking (ODPM, 2005) and Holistic Change (Branche, 2002) provide a framework of diagnosis and redesign

- ODPM (2005) includes a case study of system thinking applied at Tees Valley

- See also the Business Excellence Model (for example, EFQM), Balanced Score Card (see for example Kaplan and Norton, 1996) and Value Creation (VBM, see for example **www.vbsoloutions.co.uk\model.htm**)

- For change management, see the Audit Commission website **www.audit-commission.gov.uk/changehere**

- See also the IDeA website **www.idea.gov.uk** and search on change management.

Under Best Value Reviews, value for money may be seen as producing a range of quantitative and qualitative outputs across a range of services which collectively deliver the desired outcomes for the best possible cost (CIH, 2007b.3) In terms of maintenance services this means that organisations must consider the cost of inputs, efficiency and effectiveness when judging service value, and look at the whole system to make sure there is an optimum relationship between costs, inputs, outputs and outcomes.

There are two common errors to avoid when looking at how the client function is carried out. The first is to believe that poor customer service can be transformed by structural change. Organisational structure is a result of service design. It is a consequence not a driver of change.

The second error is to believe that poor communication is the source of most poor service, and that it can be resolved by investment in IT systems. Organisations should examine the way their service is being delivered from the customer experience. Improvement will grow from understanding how the process works, and which stages add value to the customer experience.

A systems thinking approach

Systems thinking is one approach to problem solving that considers each individual stage of a process in conjunction with the overall system or entire process. In other words it looks at the process from 'end to end'.

A systems thinking approach seeks to understand why and where delays and problems occur in the context of:

- How it fits into the whole process
- How the linkages and interactions between elements contribute to the entirety of the system or process.

For the repairs and maintenance service this would encompass the whole process from the very first point of contact from a customer reporting a repair, through the inspection and completion of work stages. A systems thinking approach requires effective communication between all departments, partners and contractors in order to avoid a silo effect, and promote input and suggestions from all staff.

Adopting a systems thinking approach can help to:

- Identify stages in the process where there are delays and blockages, as a result of the actual process or individual contractor/supplier performance
- Increase communication and joint working across all departments
- Demonstrate how small changes to one stage of the process, can be catalytic in the creation of large changes at other stages of the process, more so in complex systems
- Provide an opportunity to test how changes to one area of the system impact on the overall process; identifying if improvements in one area of a system can adversely affect another area of the same system or process.

Flagship Housing Group – Systems thinking model

Flagship Housing Group started their systems thinking journey in August 2005. Based on their learning, Flagship has remodelled many areas of work to create an organisation focused on front-line service delivery through empowered staff who have moved to a fully generic way of working with customers within 'patch' sizes based on the demands from tenants.

The starting point for Flagship was to consider how the repairs service was delivered from their customers' perspective. In doing this, they learned that customers do not care whether the service was 'responsive' or 'planned' – the customers called it 'I Want a Fix' and what was important was having the right fix, at the right time for them.

Following this, the processes were analysed and approximately 80% of what was done did was waste work from the customers' point of view. Waste work included duplicating, batching, filing, inspecting and surveying. What the customer actually 'valued' was Flagship saying that they would fix a problem, arriving to fix it when they said they would, and the problem staying fixed.

Flagship looked at the way they were working (their 'system') and identified the reasons for the waste work. This meant looking at existing operating principles and deciding if they were appropriate to meet the needs of customers.

Traditional principles and methodology were thrown away. Flagship stopped trying to complete repairs within a certain timeframe, as they found the focus of staff was on doing whatever it took to meet the deadline, rather than doing 'what mattered' for the customer.

In a redesigned approach, the customer talks to the operative who will do the work (the expert) and a conversation takes place about what the customer needs. In the new way of working for instance, if a kitchen needs replacing it is done at the time, rather than being repaired in the short term and being replaced when it has reached the top of a list managed by a planned maintenance team.

In the old way of working, typical repairs included multiple visits to the property – with pre and post inspections by the RSL staff, a couple of visits by operatives, perhaps the contractors' supervisors going along too. Each visit required the tenant to be at home. Now, with the operative empowered to make decisions, everyone who is needed to go to the property goes at the same time. This means that pre and post inspections are unnecessary and inconvenience to the customer is minimised.

Getting the operative talking to the tenant from the outset and empowering the operative to make the decisions about the works needed, resolved the issue of applying a 'blanket approach' and treating all customers the same. Now each customer sets their own standard in terms of when the work is done (regardless of traditional 'priorities' given to jobs). Because the expert is making decisions about the works required, the service is perceived as a more positive experience for customers.

→

Flagship have experienced a group wide reduction in maintenance costs to pre-September 2003 levels; this is despite around an increase in stock of 350 properties over the previous year.

Prior to implementing this new way of working a job, when viewed from a customers' perspective, took an average of 124 days to complete; meant multiple visits to the property and the job rarely 'stayed fixed', all because the right decision was not made by the expert.

Since redesign, jobs are completed on average within 9.5 days. 88% of jobs are completed with one visit to the property (single visit fix) and 98% of repairs stay fixed, ensuring the right decision has been made at the beginning.

Home Housing Association – Process review

Home's formal review of responsive repairs began with an initial 'picture' of the system from the perspective of the customer, starting with a quantitative analysis of the type and frequency of calls to the call centre. It was found that there were two types: 'value' calls and 'failure' calls. A value call was essentially first time calls to report a fault. A failure call was a customer chasing because the association had not responded. Of the 542 calls each day, 40 per cent were failure calls.

Home then looked at the work flow through the system, including time taken from fault report to completion, from the tenants' point of view. A key finding was that the service was set up to raise, complete or cancel individual jobs rather than solve tenants' repairs problems. Therefore, in terms of performance indicators, the individual jobs were being completed in target time, but customer feedback was poor.

Home started a review, involving staff across departments and levels, which looked at the 'whole job' rather than the components. The review team were asked to look at ways to eliminate waste and consider the service from the tenants' point of view. The new process that evolved was tested against the purpose of measure: reducing the end-to-end time taken to complete a repair to the customers' satisfaction.

Home also identified the bonus system as a major issue standing in the way of delivering an appointments system. The process review resulted in the workforce advocating the removal of bonuses. This made change easier, resulted in more predictable budgets and removed inefficiencies caused by the distortions of the bonus system.

The detailed changes that resulted included: a switch to specialist local call centres, empowerment of operatives, use of generic codes and replacement of bonuses with salaries.

9.7 The value of process review

It is a good idea for housing organisations to look closely at their processes. The existing ones may be overly bureaucratic, with too much paper, too many transactions, and too many opportunities for error. Process review is a good way to focus on changing this. It provides a framework for analysis and a mechanism for implementation. The general lessons to be drawn from those organisations that have adopted some form of process redesign are:

- Identifying key business streams and undertaking fundamental reviews of individual processes is a very effective way of delivering service improvement
- When defining the scope of the repairs process, embrace the whole of the maintenance cycle. A broad definition of process helps to look at services in a more holistic way
- Include the service offered across the whole association – sheltered housing and supported housing as well as general needs tenants
- Get the right mix of skills on the redesign team
- Lead from the top – commitment at director level is vital
- Focus on an evidence-based analysis, with measurable objectives and outcomes
- Define and agree critical success factors from the outset
- Define and prioritise the legal and regulatory framework governing the process under review
- Set demanding initial requirements – halving costs, doubling speed, targets which require radical thought
- Ensure that all options are kept open
- Seek to avoid implementation friction. Involve the key players in the process review, and manage passive delay. Active disagreement is better than false consensus.

The simplification that emerges from a good process review is likely to deliver efficiency gains by default. Indeed the opportunity should be taken to set demanding targets for reducing the number of transactions in a typical process. A detailed mapping of an existing process will show complexity and undocumented exception handling, with a large number of 'transactions' (inputs and outputs). A redesigned process, focusing on a significantly-reduced number of transactions, will promise to deliver a more reliable service, possibly at lower cost. However, the whole purpose of process review is to challenge the way things are done. In the case of responsive repairs, for example, the starting point for a better service is not with the detail of converting a fault report into a completed repair with the minimum of effort – albeit this is desirable in itself. The bigger questions are, for example, whether demand on the responsive repair service can be reduced, and whether needs can be met in some other way. Get answers to the big questions first. No one benefits from a more efficient process that is doing the wrong thing.

Summary

- Change is not easy to deliver, and being in a constant state of change is not necessarily a good thing. Other things do not get done while change is happening. These opportunity costs are not necessarily recognised. Change is necessary, but there should not be an obsession with structure and process at the expense of good management and simple service improvement.

- Service review should be an integral part of asset management and continuous improvement. The views of tenants should be taken into account in terms of problem definition and service specification.

- It is vital that the senior management team provide leadership, commitment and a clear set of priorities.

- Processes should be reviewed systematically and analytically. Methodologies like Business Process review (BPR) and Systems Thinking provide a helpful framework.

- The measure of service quality is about outcomes, but process design is interested in inputs. The organisation might be looking for the lowest level of input to deliver a consistently high level of service. In a diverse sector it is unreasonable to expect delivery costs to be the same in all organisations, and some will have higher costs because of their client group. At a business level it is important to acknowledge this and reflect it in the way services are planned and measured.

CHAPTER 10

CHECKLISTS AND ACTIONS

The aim of this guide is to help housing organisations improve their repairs and maintenance service. Previous chapters have drawn on examples of organisations working hard towards this aim and defined some qualities and characteristics of a good repairs service. However, it is not possible to provide a definitive summary of the actions that need to be taken in order to deliver an excellent service. There is great variety in the way services are delivered, and different approaches can produce equally acceptable results. Therefore this final chapter brings together the principles to be considered rather than being prescriptive about the way repairs and maintenance services should be run.

10.1 Responsive repairs

There is no single formula for delivering a successful responsive repairs service – it has to be designed to fit local circumstances. But there are key characteristics which tend to be shared by organisations delivering a good repairs service:

Objectives
- A central and long-term commitment to service quality from the Council or Board and from senior management
- Service development informed by a thorough understanding of tenant needs and current circumstances, and measured against good practice advice
- A consistent aim to exceed any service targets set by regulation and inspection.

Strategy
- Delivery costs minimised by working on the supply chain, reducing the cost of materials and working jointly to improve practice
- Collaboration between housing organisations to achieve more efficient and effective solutions
- Improvements in the role of managing services delivered by other agencies

- Investment in, and effective use of, better information systems together with investing resources in the management of change
- A sustained effort to reduce demand for the responsive repair service.

Process

- A process that has been radically simplified to reduce administrative costs and reduce paper
- Intelligent analysis of data to understand and resolve questions of quality and cost
- Savings through running more efficient call centres, handling higher volumes of calls
- Operating an appointments system
- Using operatives that are multi-skilled and work with stocked vans.

While these are characteristics common to many successful responsive repairs services, the method of delivery varies considerably. However, there are some common messages about service quality:

- Operate and manage call centres professionally to achieve best customer service at lowest cost
- Make customer contact easy, but also keep it as simple as possible. Ensure all fault reports are ultimately directed through a single preferred channel, usually the call centre
- Consider the benefits of co-locating staff taking repairs reports with those carrying out the repairs service. The organisation should decide whether the corporate goals of customer service and reduced overheads are compromised by the advantages for the responsive repair service of co-location
- Establish what tenants want from an appointment system, then make it work and monitor the system very carefully
- Consider what might be done to improve the keeping of appointments. Would it help if text messaging was used to confirm next-day appointments?
- Invest heavily in training at all levels across the whole process, from call centre to operative, and ensure that training is continuous
- Consider the potential to improve efficiency and customer satisfaction by arranging for operatives to work within defined areas, increasing the opportunity for tenants and workforce to get to know each other
- Design a process which aims for zero errors, but provides for error handling, and create a culture that solves the problem and learns from the experience.

The table overleaf sets out a checklist of questions to ask about the way the current responsive repairs process is working.

Responsive repairs

Is it easy to see how well the service is performing? Is repairs data analysed to gain knowledge about stock performance?	What work is delayed? How many call-backs; what are the outlier costs; are there exceptional costs for particular areas or components? Can tenants see the same performance information?
How good is the process for reporting repairs?	Do tenants rate it as a good service? Does the right information get collected, and does the job get done without the tenant having to chase? Are information systems being used to their full extent to allocate the work, to schedule appointments and cut out paperwork?
Is full use being made of the complaints procedure to identify areas of service improvement.	Can it be demonstrated that lessons have been learnt?
Could the web service be improved to allow tenants to report faults in a structured way?	Can tenants see the progress of these repairs?
How well does the work get done?	Does a multi-skilled operative arrive at the agreed time and do the work to the tenants satisfaction at the first visit? Is technology used to its full extent to support mobile working, to maintain van stock, and to deliver up-to-date performance data as part of the process?
Is web-browser software used to its fullest extent?	Is the flow of data to and from external contractors paper-free?
Are problems of access minimised by text message reminders to tenants?	Are there other opportunities to minimise failed appointments?
Are tenants contacted immediately after the work is finished to check that they are satisfied?	If this information is collected, is it then used? Is the satisfaction information combined with property data to build up a more detailed understanding of the demand for responsive repairs, and is this helping to increase the proportion of work done on a planned basis?
Is there good information about tenants and is this available to service providers?	What has been done to match the service to their disparate needs?
What work is done as responsive repairs?	Is there a known real cost of doing each repair? This is contractor plus client-side costs.
What is being done to reduce the demand for responsive repairs?	What work can be switched from responsive to planned? Can minor works be done by area caretakers, or would tenants like help to do some repairs themselves? Could an annual property visit reduce overall demand? And is there any merit in incentives and loyalty schemes?

10.2 Void works

While the term 'void' is useful within housing organisations, it means different things to different people. For tenants and potential tenants it is a possible solution to their housing need. For housing management it is an opportunity to provide someone with a home while minimising rent loss. Asset management sees this rent loss as having an impact on portfolio performance. For maintenance, the void is an opportunity to do work on the property.

These different views are not in serious conflict, but the balance must be clear. The property must be relet quickly in the interests of need and economy. This means getting as much notice as possible of an impending void, planning the minimum work needed to relet the property, and doing other works after the new tenancy has begun.

The void process tends to go wrong when responsibility is ill-defined. It should be very clear who is managing the process; the criteria for success should be clear; and the resources to succeed should be available. If, for example, void works are a secondary priority for contractors, there should no surprise when this leads to delayed handovers.

The table below sets out a checklist of the type of questions to ask about the way the current void process is working.

Void repairs

Does the organisation know how much a void costs (void works and rent loss) and the type of work done in order to relet?	
If major works are done at relet, are these done on the same rates as the planned programme?	
Is there a standard for void works? Does it include environmental measures?	Is this applied consistently?
Is there a clear strategy on this standard?	Is it only the minimum work necessary to relet the property? Can other works, for example to meet the decent homes standard, be done after the tenant has moved in? If its cheaper to do the work while the property is void, can a real saving be demonstrated?
Are new tenants always asked what they think of the property when they moved in?	If so, what is done with this information?
Are people in supported accommodation asked what they think of the accommodation?	→

Has everything been done to encourage tenants to give proper notice of termination?	Is property inspected before the end of the tenancy?
Have incentive payments to tenants been considered to encourage them to leave the property in good condition?	
Are there problems with managing the keys of void properties?	Has the use of key boxes been considered?
Is there real-time information about properties that are void over target, together with reasons for the delay?	Is it known if this is a common occurrence, and if so, what is being done about it?
Is data analysed to understand turnover?	Is it known what the factors are that result in a longer tenancy? Is it known what the savings would be if the average tenancy was just three to six months longer?

10.3 Planned maintenance

Planned maintenance operates within a financial framework set by the investment plan supporting priorities set out in the business plan. Detailed programmes should be established on a three to five year rolling programme of works that have been discussed with tenants and aligned with business objectives. Then the work must be procured on the best possible terms and delivered in a way that achieves high levels of tenant satisfaction. This means that tenants have been properly consulted and know the programme well in advance; the works are done to the agreed specification and at the agreed time; that co-ordination and communication are first class; and the work is undertaken to a high standard by a workforce that treats the tenants with respect. The specification has to be nailed down. Tenant liaison has to be good. The contract needs to be managed effectively. And high quality data is required both to manage the contract and to inform the future asset management strategy.

The table opposite sets out a check list of questions to ask about the way the current planned programme is working.

10.4 Cyclical maintenance

Cyclical maintenance deserves serious attention for several reasons. First, it includes some very important statutory duties, for example, gas and fire equipment servicing.

Planned maintenance

Is there a delivery plan, base on the investment plan, which shows how the quality standard will be delivered and how the work will be procured?	Has this plan been made known to avoid unnecessary responsive repairs expenditure?
What process is in place for prioritising the planned programme?	Is it open and fair, and is there a method of appeal?
Is the works completed data from planned programme flowing back to update the stock condition database so that the investment plan is revised?	
Is a partnering agreement in place?	If so, is it clear what improvements can be expected in the next twelve months and will it be possible to tell whether these improvements have been delivered?
If the stock is widely dispersed, have setting-up maintenance contracts in partnership with other social landlords been considered?	
If the organisation is small, can procurement expertise be gained by working in partnership with other housing organisations?	
What processes are in place for involving tenants in the performance assessment of planned programme contractors?	

Second, routine servicing gains a much higher profile if equipment like lifts or door entry systems acquire a reputation for unreliability. Third, routine painting, cleaning and landscaping maintenance functions have a disproportionately large impact on residents' quality of life.

To these existing reasons are two additional factors. First, the growth of mixed tenure and the need to be much better at managing service charges. Second, the potential development of thinking about preventative planned maintenance as a way of postponing major component renewal.

The table overleaf sets out a check list of questions to ask about the way the current arrangements for cyclical maintenance are working.

Cyclical maintenance

Are gas service checks being done properly?	Are systems top-class with reliable data that is being used to monitor performance? Are there well documented procedures when access has not been achieved?
Would incentives help to get gas servicing done on the first visit?	Would text message reminders help?
Is there a programme of electrical safety checks?	
Are service contracts bundled-up (for example fire alarms, door entry systems) so that everything is covered?	Does everyone knows who is responsible for routine work and out of hours emergencies?
Are tenants involved in service specification and monitoring?	
Has the cyclical programme been designed in order to reduce or delay the need for planned replacement?	
Have regular tenant led estate inspections or estate walkabouts been considered to check on cyclical maintenance and identify priorities for planned programmes?	
Has the value of estate caretakers been assessed to provide a cost effective quick local response?	
Have the whole life costs of components been identified?	Have cyclical programmes been reviewed to identify ways of reducing the need for a reactive response?
Are the costs of boiler maintenance being reduced by careful specification and value management?	Are there similar value management opportunities in other areas?
Have obligations been met under the asbestos regulations?	Is data on the presence of asbestos easily available to contractors?
Are service charge costs being calculated properly?	Is it possible to attribute responsive and cyclical costs correctly?
Is it possible to improve the way leaseholder costs are forecast?	As a minimum, are statutory obligations being met? Could more be done by way of communication, consultation and advice, both on cyclical costs and also in relation to major works?

10.5 Asset management

The meaning of asset management is in a state of transformation. Some housing organisations are at a point where their stock data is approaching the level of accuracy needed for effective planning. The software is improving to co-ordinate planned programmes, and there is evidence of integration with housing management and finance systems. There is also activity to identify stock that is expensive to maintain or is in low demand areas. And some organisations are developing strategies for the long-term re-profiling of their stock.

In the commercial sector, asset management is all about return. In social housing there is a recognition that social value comes into the equation. How this can be done is only slowly being understood. Whatever the approach, everyone has to recognise that low cost inputs can have expensive outcomes.

This is why asset management has to operate as part of housing management not as a separate operation. There is no necessary link between ownership and service provision. This means that future housing organisations could be asset management organisations, with all services provided by other external agencies. To do this in the context of social housing, however, housing management input must be enhanced to deliver key goals, not simply reduced to deliver the cheapest possible service.

In the future, housing organisations may be able to operate much more freely in the market place provided they pursue their not-for-profit goals. This means a wider involvement in a range of development activities, including market renting. It means trading in residential and non-residential property in full pursuit of a professional approach to asset management as a portfolio that should be run at maximum effective return. The difference is that this view of effective return is not a short-term return to investors, it is a long term commitment to local communities, where views are taken about the lowest input costs to achieve the best possible long-term outcomes.

The table overleaf sets out a check list of questions to ask about asset management.

10.6 Procurement

There is no single approach to procurement, but all housing organisations must be aware of government advice on partnering, collective procurement and supply chain management. This advice provides a framework within which individual solutions can be tailored.

Asset management

Is there an asset management strategy that has been validated?	Is it reviewed at least annually?
Is there reliable and up-to-date data about the condition of your housing stock?	Has the quality of this data been validated?
Are there information systems that translate this data into a forecast investment plan?	Has there been a review of all the information system requirements to support the organisation's asset management functions?
Is the investment plan refreshed annually to tie in with the budget cycle?	
Has the investment plan been analysed carefully and aligned with the business plan?	
Is there a process to challenge the investment plan?	Does it cover the cost of delivering the aspirations agreed with tenants?
Is the housing stock thought of as an asset portfolio?	If so, is portfolio performance measured? Would it be valuable to embed the idea of portfolio management within the business plan?
Has an aspirational standard been established, particularly in relationship to energy performance and sustainable communities?	Has there been consultation on this standard, and can they be funded by the business plan?
Is there an energy strategy?	
To what extent has the life-time homes standard been taken into account, and is there more that could be done to align the planned programme with the special needs of individual tenants?	
Is there a way of identifying stock that needs to be reviewed before re-investment?	Is enough known about long term trends in demand for the homes in the areas where the organisation operates?
Is there a method of option appraisal that can be applied to evaluate schemes?	
Is there an approach to neighbourhood assessment?	
Is enough being done to align the investment strategy with the local authority to support regeneration and community development?	Are there opportunities to make better use of assets through remodelling, infill or redevelopment?

Partnering is not always the right approach, and when it is adopted it is not the solution to all problems. Done well it offers the advantage of lower transaction costs, economies of scale and more control over the market. Good partnering needs commitment from all parties to do their job well in pursuit of common objectives. It is worth recognising that there will be different agendas round the table. However, the most important part of leadership is to find the areas of common interest and use these as the way to drive improvements that deliver both commercial and service gains.

In order to reduce costs, housing organisations should look at the benefits of scale. They should seek opportunities to cooperate in order to increase volume and concentrate work within areas. And they should also look for the benefits of scale through call centres, software and service partnerships.

In considering partnering, housing organisations should:

- Look seriously at the price and service gains to be obtained, but not lose sight of the need for a measurable price advantage
- Choose partners with care
- Consider taking an existing and stable working arrangement and moving it forwards towards partnering
- Remember, when looking at costs, that a contractor's low price can result in high value invoices when variations and wastage are added
- Devote time to defining performance indicators which may include defects and call backs, and ensure they can be analysed in detail
- Agree a simple form of contract
- Enter into a long-term agreement, with five years being sufficient to encourage the level of investment needed in essential areas such as the integration of information systems
- Establish what is meant by 'open book'
- Share costs and savings, but do not automatically adopt a regime of performance incentives and penalties.

Where partnering offers the right solution, circumstances might also point to the advantage of contracting out the whole service. Organisations should consider the merits of using the same contractor to do responsive and planned maintenance.

Lessons for improving materials procurement are to:

- Look for cost reductions from lower administrative and labour costs
- Reduce labour costs through better utilisation – e.g. stocked vans and minimum off-site times, including work scheduling and appointments to avoid abortive visits

- Take the opportunities for savings on materials seriously
- Treat procurement as a strategic and specialist discipline
- Recognise that supply chain management needs expertise and also scale to secure volume.

More thought needs to be given to managing the supply chain, and housing organisations should take active steps to look at the merits of collective procurement and supply chain partnering.

10.7 Performance measurement

Housing organisations not only need to improve their services, but they need to know whether they are doing so, and be able to show the extent of their improvement. The key drivers are cost control and tenant satisfaction. Housing organisations should:

- Seek to make better use of data analysis to predict and solve problems rather than just to report performance
- Ensure that there are people who have data analysis skills. If they do not exist in-house, they might be introduced through a partner organisation, an application service provider, or by outsourcing to a third party specialist
- Ensure there is an exit strategy which retains ownership of detailed transaction histories if partnerships involve using a contractor's information system. An external organisation (an 'application service provider') might be a safer option, with the data held independently of the partnering contractor.

In reviewing performance, housing organisations should:

- Measure faults not repairs
- Collect reasons why appointments are not kept
- Record tenants' requests for an inspection
- Improve measures of performance, particularly in terms of efficiency measures – whether the level of spending is giving value for money
- Benchmark against their peer groups.

Organisations should be able to demonstrate that tenants are happy with the repairs service; that the service is improving against internal PIs and peer group benchmarking; with evidence that the organisation is actively looking for improvements which will produce efficiency gains which can be devoted to better service.

10.8 Service review

Across the country, some housing organisations have radically restructured their repairs and maintenance service while others have taken a more piecemeal approach, focusing on areas where the biggest potential gains can be achieved at the lowest cost. The latter can be a valid approach. There are circumstances where solutions are fairly obvious, and the case for quick wins overwhelming.

However, there are dangers associated with a piecemeal approach, and as a minimum, all change should be informed by clear assessment and measurement, backed by proper knowledge of tenants' priorities. Innovations should not be applied without thought to the particular circumstances of individual organisations. Ideally, the right approach should be worked out from first principles, and this is the strength of process review. Housing organisations adopting this approach should:

- Undertake a fundamental review of the broadly defined maintenance function
- Seek to be radical, but do not assume that major investment is the solution
- Focus on customer service
- Ensure that the responsive repairs service is part of a holistic maintenance regime so as to shift the balance towards planned works
- Set demanding targets for service improvement and cost reduction
- Find administrative economies through more shared call centres associated with better information systems and greater use of internet reporting
- Reduce pipeline times for key elements of work with better information systems, more sophisticated works scheduling, better appointments, speedier completion and more efficient invoicing
- Aim for a simplified process, with significantly reduced transactions, as this will help to deliver a more reliable service at lower cost.

GLOSSARY

ALMO
: Arms Length Management Organisation – a company set up by a local authority to manage and improve all or part of its housing stock

Asset management
: The management of physical assets to meet the service and financial objectives of the organisation

Audit Commission
: The body that inspects local authorities in England. Their remit extends to registered housing associations

Audit Scotland
: The equivalent of the Audit Commission in Scotland, but not inspecting housing associations

Barker Review
: Review of housing supply commissioned by HM Treasury and ODPM (2004a)

BPR
: Business Process Review

Cave Review
: Review of social housing regulation in England (CLG, 2007a)

CIOB
: Chartered Institute of Building

CIH
: Chartered Institute of Housing

CBL
: Choice Based Letting

CAA
: Comprehensive Area Assessment

Client
: The NAO (2001) defines the client as the sponsor, owner and decision maker in relation to the supplier of a construction project or service

Communities Scotland
: The former regulatory body for housing associations in Scotland (see Scottish Housing Regulator)

Contractor
: A generic term used in this guide to refer to both external contractors and internal DSOs

Curtilage
: The land attached or belonging to a property

Cyclical maintenance	Work carried out on a cycle such as painting and gas safety checks
DHS	The Decent Homes Standard for homes in England
DLO	Direct Labour Organisation (see DSO below)
DSO	Direct Service Organisation (sometimes known as a DLO)
DEA	Domestic Energy Assessor
Egan Report	The Egan Report on the construction industry (DETR, 1998)
EcoHomes XB	A standard for the environmental performance of the existing housing stock
Egan Review	Review of the skills and training that are required to deliver sustainable communities
EPBD	Energy Performance in Building Directive
EPCs	Energy Performance Certificates
GIS	Geographic Information System
Gershon Review	A review of public sector efficiency commissioned by HM Treasury (2004)
HCA	Homes and Communities Agency – taking over the investment role of the Housing Corporation in England, plus English Partnerships and some functions of CLG
HHSRS	Housing health and safety rating system (ODPM, 2006)
Hills Report	An independent review of the future role of social housing in England (2007)
HIP	Home Information Pack
Housing Corporation	The government agency that regulates housing associations in England
HRA	Housing Revenue Account
Housing organisation	A generic term used in this guide to refer to providers of affordable housing
Housing Quality Standard	A generic term used in this report to include the DHS (England), SHQS (Scotland) and WHQS (Wales)
IDeA	Improvement and Development Agency
Invasive testing	The taking of core material samples (for example, asbestos testing) or works associated with inspection (for example to view footings as part of a structural survey)

Investment plan	A forecast of the costs of maintaining an organisation's housing stock. Conventionally shown over thirty years to support the business plan
JIT	Just In Time (Intelligent Programming)
KLOE	Key Lines of Enquiry
KPI	Key Performance Indicator
LSVT	Large Scale Voluntary Transfer
Latham Report	A report on the role of the team in the construction industry (1994)
Leaseholder	The owner of a flat in England and Wales. In Scotland, flat ownership is usually governed by the provisions of the title deed
LAA	Local Area Agreements – a three year local strategic partnership agreement to deliver priorities in the sustainable communities strategy
M&E	Mechanical and electrical
NHF	National Housing Federation
NAW	National Assembly for Wales
NROSH	National Register of Social Housing
NPV	Net Present Value
OT	Occupational Therapist
OFTENANT	The new regulator in England taking over from the Housing Corporation
Open book	A method of accounting under partnering which discloses all costs and time values incurred
PIR	Periodic inspection report (electrical inspections)
PDA	Personal data assistant – small handheld data collection device
Planned maintenance	The renewal or improvement of a component delivered as part of a planned programme
PFI	Private Finance Initiative
RSL	Registered Social Landlord. A body registered with the Housing Corporation in England and the equivalent regulators in Scotland and Wales
RDSAP	Reduced Data SAP (see below)

Residual valuation	Under NPV, the assumed value of an asset at the end of the appraisal period
Responsive repair	A repair to be carried out to a property because of a tenant's request, a request made on behalf of the tenant, or a repair to a common area
RTB	Right to Buy. Scheme under which most council tenants and some housing association tenants may buy their home below market value
Scottish Housing Regulator	Succeeded the regulation and inspection role of Communities Scotland on 1st April 2008
Section 106	In the context of affordable housing, a developer's contribution as part of a planning obligation (from Section 106 of the Town and Country Planning Act 1990)
Segmentation	A term used in marketing referring to the division of a group of customers or users of a particular product or service into sub-groups defined by differences in their needs or wants in relation to that product. The skill is to define the fewest possible segments that give the greatest improvement in understanding of the customer
Social housing	A generic term used in this guide to refer to homes provided by local authorities, ALMOs and RSLs
SAP	Standard Assessment Procedure – for the energy rating of dwellings
SHQS	Scottish Housing Quality Standard
Tenant	A generic term used in this guide to mean the principal customers of housing organisations. The term does not define their legal status but distinguishes them from leaseholders, owners and shared owners
VFM	Value For Money
WAG	Welsh Assembly Government
WAO	Welsh Audit Office
WHQS	Welsh Housing Quality Standard

Audit Commission (1986) *Improving council house maintenance*

Audit Commission (2002) *Learning from Inspection: Housing repairs and maintenance*

Audit Commission (2002a) *Learning from Inspection: Housing repairs and maintenance handbook*

Audit Commission (2003) *Promoting positive practice: Audit Commission Housing Review, Part II*

Audit Commission (2004) *Stock investment and asset management KLOE*

Audit Commission (2004a) *Assistive Technology: Independence and well-being*

Audit Commission (2005) *Prospects for improvement KLOE*

Audit Commission (2005a) *Gas safety guidance note for landlords*

Audit Commission (2006) *Choosing Well: Analysing the costs and benefits of choice in local public service*

Audit Commission (2006a) *Partnering in responsive and planned repairs: Efficiency Pack*

Audit Commission (2008) *Better Buys: Improving housing association procurement practice.*

Branche, A (2002) *How organisations work: Taking a holistic approach to enterprise health*

BRE (2006) *EcoHomes XB: The environmental rating for existing housing: Assessment guidance notes*

Byatt Review (2001) *Delivering better service for citizens*

CIH (2003) *Leasehold Management: A good practice guide*

CIH (2005) *Right first time: How housing associations are improving their responsive repairs*

CIH (2005a) *Is big really best: Or can small and friendly deliver?*

CIH (2005b) *ALMOs: A new future for council housing*

CIH (2005c) *Sheltered and retirement housing: A good practice guide*

CIH (2006) *The future of regulation of the affordable housing sector in England*

CIH (2006a) *The costs and benefits of groups, mergers and partnerships*

CIH (2007) *Delivering housing strategy through local area agreements*

CIH (2007a) *The rationalisation of housing association stock*

CIH (2007b) *Embedding value for money in housing association services*

CIH (2008) Good Practice Briefing No. 32 *Customer insight*

CIH (2008a) Good Practice Briefing No. 33 *Managing voids*

CRE (2003) *Public procurement and race equality*

CRE (2003a) *Race equality and procurement in local government*

CLG (2006) *A decent home: Definition and guidance for implementation*

CLG (2006a) *From decent homes to sustainable communities: A discussion paper*

CLG (2006b) *Strong and prosperous communities: The local government White Paper*

CLG (2006c) *Code for sustainable homes*

CLG (2007) *Implementing decent homes in the social sector*

CLG (2007a) *Every tenant matters: A review of social housing regulation* The Cave Review

CLG (2007b) *Homes for the future: More affordable, more sustainable*

CLG (2007c) *The new performance framework for local authorities and local authority partnerships: Single set of national indicators.*

Communities Scotland (2004) *The Scottish housing quality standard: Delivery plan guidance*

Communities Scotland (2004b) *Managing housing voids: The impact of low demand properties*

Communities Scotland (2005) *Key themes from inspection: Tenant participation*

Communities Scotland (2006) *How to gather views on service quality: Guidance for social landlords*

Communities Scotland et al (2006a) *Performance standards for social landlords and homelessness functions* Communities Scotland, Convention of Scottish Local Authorities and Scottish Federation of Housing Associations

Communities Scotland (2006b) *A legislation and literature review of health and safety for social landlords* (research report and précis)

Communities Scotland (2006c) *Gas Safety Matters*

Communities Scotland (2006d) *Procurement guide for use by registered social landlords*

Communities Scotland (2007) *Sustainable housing design guide*

Communities Scotland (2007a) *Key themes from inspections*

Communities Scotland (2007b) *Equalities in practice*

Constructing Excellence (2002) *Rethinking the Construction Client*

Crerar Review (2007) *Report of the Independent Review of Regulation, Audit, Inspection and Complaints Handling of Public Service in Scotland* The Scottish Government

DETR (2000) *Quality and choice: A decent home for all*

DETR (2000a) *Collecting, managing and using housing stock information*

Egan Report (1998) *Rethinking construction* DETR

Future Shape of the Sector Commission (2006) *Growing up: Questions and challenges to promote successful housing association growth*

Gershon Review (2004) *Releasing resources for the front line: Independent review of public sector efficiency* HM Treasury

GLA (2007) *The construction industry in London and diversity performance* Greater London Authority

Green, H (2004) *Staff recruitment and retention: A good practice guide*, CIH

Hammer, M and Champy, J (1993) *Re-engineering the corporation: A manifesto for business revolution* Harper Collins

HM Treasury (2004) *Delivering stability: Securing our future housing needs* Barker Review of Housing Supply

HM Treasury (2006) *The future role of the third sector in social and economic regeneration* (with Cabinet Office)

Hills, J (2007) *Ends and means: The future roles of social housing in England*, ESRC Research Centre for Analysis of Social Exclusion

HAIAF (2006) *Internal Audit Programme Guide: Partnering Arrangements* Housing Association Internal Audit Forum

HAIAF (2006a) *Internal Audit Programme Guide: Procurement and European Union Procurement Rules* Housing Association Internal Audit Forum

HouseMark (2008) *Embracing diversity: A good practice guide*

HouseMark (2008a) How to develop and monitor local performance measures: a guide for tenants and landlords

Housing Corporation (2002) *Good practice guide for RSLs assessing the performance of their DLOs*

Housing Corporation (2002a) *(How) are you being served? A good practice guide on complaints handling in housing associations.*

Housing Corporation (2003) *Inspection uncovered: Repairs and maintenance services*

Housing Corporation (2003a) *Inspection uncovered: Equality and diversity*

Housing Corporation (2003b) *Inspection uncovered: Tenant involvement*

Housing Corporation (2003c) *Assessing procurement*

Housing Corporation (2003d) *A toolkit of indicators of sustainable communities: Third edition*

Housing Corporation (2004) *Involvement policy for the housing association sector*

Housing Corporation (2004a) *Assessing housing association compliance of the 'Involvement policy for the housing association sector*

Housing Corporation (2005) *The regulatory code and guidance*

Housing Corporation (2006) *Delivering change through involvement: Consultation Paper*

Housing Corporation (2006a) *Survey of existing housing association tenants*

Housing Corporation (2006b) *Housing associations and movement to target rents 2004 to 2005*, Sector Study 47

Housing Corporation (2006c) *Procurement strategy for the supply of affordable homes*

Housing Corporation (2007) *Unlocking the door: Delivering more homes from the comprehensive spending review 2007*

Housing Corporation (2007a) *Global accounts of housing associations 2006*

Housing Corporation (2007b) *The rationalisation of housing association stock: A guide and toolkit.*

Housing Corporation (2007c) *Meeting the decent home standard* Sector Study 58

Housing Corporation (2007d) *Energy performance certificates: Interim Guidance for Housing Associations*

Housing Forum (2000) *How to survive partnering: It won't bite*

HQN (2007) *Determining the comparative value of responsive repairs*

IDeA (2006) *Procurement Essentials*

JRF (1996) *Handyperson schemes: Making them work* Nigel Appleton

JRF (2002) *Achieving community benefits through contracts: Law, policy and practice* MacFarlane, R and Cook, M, Policy Press

Kaplan, R S and Norton, D P (1996) *Balanced scorecard: Translating strategies into action* Harvard Press

Kotler, J (1998) *Marketing management: Analysis, planning, implementation and control* Prentice Hall

Larkin, A (2000) *Asset management strategies: A review of asset management strategies of housing associations in England and social housing providers in Australia* Metropolitan Housing Trust and The Housing Corporation

Latham Report (1994) *Constructing the team* HMSO

LGA (2005) *Putting the customer first* Local Government Association.

Maclennan, D et al (1989) *The nature and effectiveness of housing management in England*, HMSO

Maclennan, D (2007) *Housing connections* Search, Issue 45, Joseph Rowntree Foundation

McLean, S (1999) *Repairs for all: How social landlords can extend their repairs service to local home owners* JRF.

National Assembly for Wales (2001) *Best value for registered social landlords: A consultation paper*

National Assembly for Wales (2006) *Regulatory Code for Housing Associations Registered in Wales*

National Audit Office (2001) *Modernising Construction*

NCA (2007) *Guidance note: Measuring capital works efficiency* National Change Agency

NCC (2005) *Playlist for public services* National Consumer Council

NCC (2006) *Developing measures of satisfaction for local services* National Consumer Council

NCC (2007) *Customer satisfaction with local services* National Consumer Council and Local Government Association

NHF (2000) *Running Status: A guide to undertaking the standard satisfaction survey*

NHF (2002) *Stock condition surveys: A guide for registered social landlords*

NHF (2004) *Best practice in maintenance*

NHF (2004a) *Delivering decent homes: The experience of housing associations in England*

NHF (2004b) *Housing investment appraisal* Dave Treanor and John Walker

NHF (2004c) *Asset management case studies: Asset management initiatives network project*

NHF (2005) *Service charges: A guide for housing associations*

NHF (2006) *What tenants want: Report of the Tenant Involvement Commission* National Consumer Council

NHF (2007) *Guide to the EU procurement rules* (2nd edition)

NHF (2008) *Your place or mine? Residents and property services*

ODPM (2003) Incentives and beyond: The transferability of the Irwell Valley Gold Service to other social landlords

ODPM (2004) *Skills for sustainable communities: The Egan Review*

ODPM (2004a) *Delivering stability: Securing our future housing needs*

ODPM (2005) *A systematic approach to service improvement: Evaluating system thinking in housing*

ODPM (2005a) *Sustainable communities: Homes for all*

ODPM (2006) *Housing health and safety rating system: Operating guidance*

OPSR (2004) *Customer satisfaction with key public services* Office of Public Sector Reform (www.cabinetoffice.gov.uk/opsr)

PEP (1997) *Caretaking Plus: Research into enhanced caretaking to deliver responsive housing maintenance and management*

Prior, J and Nowak, F (2005) *Repair it with effective partnering: Guide to contractual relationships for cost effective responsive maintenance* BRE

Scottish Executive (2000) *Report of the Joint Future Group*

Scottish Executive (2005) *Homes for Scotland's people: A Scottish housing policy statement*

Scottish Executive (2007) *Statistical Bulletin: Housing Service*

Scottish Government (2007) *Firm Foundations: The future of housing in Scotland.*

SFHA (2005) *Housing associations duties as landlords: Procedures for access to undertake annual gas safety inspections* SFHA Good Practice Guide

Slatter, P (2001) *After the crossroads: Housing associations as community investors* JRF

Welsh Assembly Government (2001) *Better homes for people in Wales: A national housing strategy for Wales*

Welsh Assembly Government (2002) *Guidance for local authority housing stock business planning*

Welsh Assembly Government (2002a) *The Welsh Housing Quality Standard : Guidance for local authorities on the assessment process and achievement of the standard*

Welsh Assembly Government (2006) *Draft national resident participation strategy for Wales*

Welsh Assembly Government (2006a) *An evaluation of best value guidance for registered social landlords*

Welsh Assembly Government (2006b) *Welsh Housing Statistics 2005*

Welsh Assembly Government (2006c) Making the connections – *delivering beyond boundaries: Transforming public service in Wales*

Welsh Assembly Government (2006d) *Beyond Boundaries: Citizen-centred local services for Wales* (The Beecham Review)

Welsh Audit Office (2005) *Housing Key Lines of Enquiry*

WLGA (2007) Repairs and improvement: A Better Housing Services toolkit prepared by the Welsh Local Government Association

Web references

http://environment.uwe.ac.uk/hcond

www.audit-commission.gov.uk/changehere

www.audit-commission.gov.uk/changehere/ecohomes

www.bcha.co.uk/homes/sustainable.html

www.cabinetoffice.gov.uk/opsr

www.ccinw.com/images/demos/003LHT.pdf

www.cih.org/housingmanual

www.cih.org/policy/RightFirstTime05.pdf

www.communities.gov.uk/housing/decenthomes/

www.communities.gov.uk/documents/planningandbuilding/pdf/319282

www.constructingexcellence.org.uk/tools/gamptoolkit/process.jsp

www.diag.org.uk

www.eeph.org.uk/partnership/index.cfm?mode=view&category_id=24

www.energysavingtrust.org.uk/housingbuildings/localauthorities/

www.esd.co.uk/has/Good_Practice_Interim_Guidance_HAs.pdf

www.greenstreet.org.uk

www.housingcorp.gov.uk/upload/pdf/EcoHomes-XB.pdf

www.housingcorp.gov.uk/upload/pdf/HHSRS_Resource_Summary.pdf

www.jrf.org.uk/housingandcare/lifetimehomes

www.ogc.uk/index.asp?docid=1001034

www.scotland.gov.uk/topics

www.sheffieldhomes.org.uk/performance-at-your-fingertips

www.sustainablehomes.co.uk/pdf/GPGRefurbs.pdf

www.valuingcomplaints.org.uk

www.vbsoloutions.co.uk/model.htm

www.wlga.gov.uk/housingtoolkits

Useful Web Links

4ps (Local Government Delivery Project)	www.4ps.gov.uk
Audit Commission	www.audit-commission.gov.uk
Cabinet Office	www.cabinetoffice.gov.uk

Chartered Institute of Housing	www.cih.org
Communities and Local Government	www.communities.gov.uk
Communities Scotland	www.communitiesscotland.gov.uk
Constructing Excellence	www.constructingexcellence.org.uk
Energy Saving Trust	www.energysavingtrust.org.uk
Equality and Human Rights Commission	www.equalityhumanrights.com
Health and Safety Executive	www.hse.gov.uk
Housing Corporation	www.housingcorp.gov.uk
Housing Ombudsman Service	www.ihos.org.uk
Improvement and Development Agency	www.idea.gov.uk
Joseph Rowntree Foundation	www.jrf.org.uk
Kier Group	www.kier.co.uk
Leasehold Advisory Service	www.lease-advice.org
Lifetime Homes	www.lifetimehomes.org.uk
Local Government Association	www.lga.gov.uk
Local Government Ombudsman	www.lgo.org.uk
Local Government Performance	www.bvpi.gov.uk
National Change Agent Housing	www.ncahousing.org.uk
National Housing Federation	www.housing.org.uk
Northern Ireland Housing Executive	www.nihe.gov.uk
Office of Government Commerce	www.ogc.gov.uk
Scottish Government	www.scotland.gov.uk
Scottish Housing Regulator	www.scottishhousingregulator.gov.uk
Sustainable Homes	www.sustainablehomes.co.uk
Welsh Local Government Association	www.wlga.gov.uk